Psychiatry
IN PASTORAL PRACTICE

Psychiatry
IN PASTORAL PRACTICE

W. L. NORTHRIDGE

LONDON

EPWORTH PRESS

© EPWORTH PRESS 1938
FIRST PUBLISHED 1938
SECOND IMPRESSION 1938
THIRD IMPRESSION 1939
SECOND EDITION 1947
THIRD EDITION 1968
PUBLISHED BY
EPWORTH PRESS
Book Steward: Frank H. Cumbers

SBN 7162 0039 2

SET IN MONOTYPE BASKERVILLE AND PRINTED IN
GREAT BRITAIN BY THE CAMELOT PRESS LTD
LONDON AND SOUTHAMPTON

To Nigel and David

Foreword

Over forty years ago, Dr Northridge, then principal of the Methodist Theological College in Belfast, came over to Leeds to attend a demonstration which I gave before a group of doctors and ministers showing the value of hypnosis in the work of both professions. We became friends at once and our friendship deepened with the years until it was interrupted by his recent death.

It is a privilege to commend this book. It is not a re-hash of his earlier work called *Psychology and Pastoral Practice*, a book which had a deservedly wide circulation. This book has been completely re-written and brought up to date.

It is a most valuable contribution to a matter which at last is getting recognition in high places, namely the *necessity* of co-operation in the art of healing between doctors and ministers.

This is not only true in regard to psychosomatic illnesses— those which originate in the mind but produce symptoms in the body—but even in diseases the origin of which appears to be wholly physical. To use a phrase of Shattuck, it is as important to know 'what sort of fellah has a germ as it is to know what sort of germ has a fellah'. More and more it will be found that the positive assertions of undenominational and liberal religion are therapeutic factors of the greatest importance, value and significance. Guilty feeling, to quote only one example, can lie behind all manner of illnesses, even those with physical symptoms. No pills can dispel those feelings, though drugs may obscure them. No psychoanalysis can do more than reveal their presence. But the loving forgiveness of God, mediated through human speech and action, can *eradicate* them and end the misery of a patient who may have suffered for years.

Ministers or deaconesses who desire to make their pastoral ministry far more valuable, not to say thrilling, should study this book for its insights and understanding of human nature.

Dr Northridge is the ideal guide in these matters. Read him, for instance, on the matter of pre-marital sex, in Chapter 10, or on Sin, Moral Disease and Morbid Guilt (Chapter 5), or on Ministering to the Aged, Sick and Bereaved (Chapter

13). He had magnificent intellectual equipment, unerring insight, a most endearing humility, and above all a compassion and real love for people in any kind of trouble.

The chapter headings show that he was not just concerned with healing the sick but with 'all those who in this transitory life are in trouble, sorrow, need, sickness or any other adversity'.

I have nothing but praise for this splendid book and I commend it without reservation to all who seek to equip themselves to help their fellows.

LESLIE D. WEATHERHEAD

Contents

Contents

Preface

Not being a professional psychiatrist it may seem presumptuous on my part to use the word 'psychiatry' in the title of a book on pastoral psychology. The justification for doing so is that this subject has been one of supreme interest to me since I was introduced to its study during my university training. At that time Freudianism was only in its infancy, and I became impressed at once with its importance in the practical and pastoral training of men for the Christian ministry. Throughout a long ministry I have also come to see the importance of psychiatry in turning the attention of ministers to the specific needs of individuals, rather than to people in the mass. Of the two—preaching and pastoral work—I have been compelled to view the latter as of the greater importance.

Throughout my ministry I have also been privileged to work in close association with many Christian psychiatrists—men who recognized the value of religion, side by side with psychiatry—in the healing of minds diseased. From these I have learnt much, as well as from a concentrated study over the years of significant developments in this particular field. I have gleaned most, however, from experience of listening to, and helping, those who have been afflicted with various types of nervous, mental, and spiritual illness.

This book replaces *Psychology and Pastoral Practice*—now out of print. Instead of revising that book at the request of my publishers, I have felt it necessary to rewrite it completely. Chapters are added on subjects not discussed in the earlier book, while others have been omitted. The book was translated into modern Greek for use in the Greek Orthodox Church in connexion with the training of students for the ministry. The translator, Professor Savas Agourides, then of the University of Thessalonica, contributed an introduction, from which I make the following quotations:

'Very little was done in Greece to give Priests for the Greek Orthodox Church any grounding in pastoral psychology. This was all the more remarkable when it is recalled that throughout most countries this study almost completely fills the scene of contemporary thought.

'There is no doubt that a training in Dogmatic Theology, in the Scriptures, and in Church History, form the essential foundations of the education of a minister of the Church. To what extent, however, will such training alone enable him to meet the problems of the alcoholic, the drug addict, the sufferer from inferiority, or the unforgivable-sin delusion? How is the minister to handle the very difficult and varied problems of youth, the multitude of sexual abnormalities and confusions that upset their minds, and how is he to distinguish between sin and moral disease?

'The Christian Church has at its disposal a complete treasury of principles and methods which have the highest therapeutic value if only they were more fully understood. Christ and His apostles not only knew the depths of the human soul and its needs, but also tended the suffering. The Church continued this work, not, however, with the same zeal as in Apostolic times. Certainly in some of the Fathers, particularly in those called 'Ascetics', there is a remarkable insight into the problems of the human soul—an insight which sometimes has a kinship with contemporary analysis of these problems.

'The writer of this book makes it clear throughout that in the restoration of the health of the sick by psychological means the final aim of the treatment is to produce a healthy religious faith. This and other reflections led us to make the translation of this book into Greek. We chose it among many others of the same kind because we considered that it includes in its scope the most important material, and has the fewest disadvantages. Throughout a long ministry the author has served his denomination as pastor, teacher, and mental healer. His experience has been distilled into this valuable work.'

My friend of many years, the Rev. Dr Leslie D. Weatherhead, O.B.E., has contributed a foreword to the present book, as he so kindly did to its predecessor. To him I am grateful, as also to another friend, the Rev. S. J. W. Nabney, B.A., who read the draft manuscript and assisted with the correction of the proofs. I am indebted also to Dr Stafford Knox, a well-known psychiatrist, who read the sections on the symptoms of nervous and psychotic disorders.

ONE

Doctor-Minister Co-operation

Co-operation between the medical profession and the Church in the care of the sick is one of the most important religious developments of our time. The idea is by no means new; but, until recently, actual co-operation has been left largely to isolated groups led by a few enthusiasts—whose judgements have not always been reliable. Now, both in America and Britain, institutes of 'Religion and Medicine' have been set up on a national scale, and many journals devoted to the subject are published quarterly. Moreover, important conferences between doctors and ministers are regularly taking place. In these are discussed many problems relating to health in its broadest aspects, and the extent to which collaboration can be useful in the treatment of the sick in body, mind, or spirit.

This co-operative ministry has been greatly stimulated by the deeper understanding of personality, which we owe largely to the researches of 'depth psychologists'. These have emphasized (what as a matter of fact underlies Hebrew psychology) the *unity* of the self. This will receive frequent reference in succeeding pages. Here it is necessary only to say that actual experience conclusively proves the extent to which any disturbance on one side of one's personality can, and does, affect the others. An emotional conflict, for example, can set up bodily symptoms, and any organic deficiency can have profound effects on mental functioning. Furthermore, arising from this fact of the unity of the self, is the concept of healing as related to the entire personality and not merely to that of a particular limb or organ of the body. Thus doctors are no longer baffled by such a phenomenon as the inability of a patient whose leg has been fractured in an accident, to walk even after the fracture has been healed. They know that when this occurs there is a 'fracture' of the mind which also has to receive attention before the *person* is restored to health. To heal a limb is one thing; to heal the person is often another. Indeed, such situations (which are by no means hypothetical) require investigation into the motives for the accident. This means that what are called 'accidents' may actually be the outcome of unconscious wishes such as Freud discussed in his *Psychopathology of Everyday Life*. In this connexion considerable attention has been devoted in recent years to the subject of 'accident proneness'.

Two conditions must be complied with if co-operation is to reach still further development. The first is that doctors should be interested in religion, and should appreciate its therapeutic value. In later chapters we shall, of course, make it plain that religion, in some of its forms, can itself be not only a neurosis, but a factor in creating nervous ill-health. We shall, therefore, have to draw a sharp distinction between neurotic types of religion and the religion of healthy-mindedness. No doctor can be expected to co-operate with the Church whose tenets are extremely obscurantist, or with any form of religion which, from its nature, has a disintegrating effect on the personality.

Doctors, moreover, must be satisfied that ministers who are eager to engage in this work must have adequate training in the field of pastoral psychology, as well as in the more academic studies.

On the other hand ministers cannot be enthusiastic over the idea of co-operation with doctors who are hostile, or indifferent, to the foundation beliefs of Christians. We are often asked by patients who are advised to seek psychiatric help whether the particular psychiatrist is a 'Christian' or not. Now we know that it is assumed that no psychiatrist, no matter what school of psychiatry he favours, attempts to interfere with the religious beliefs of his patients. At the same time it is difficult for one who is anti-Christian not to influence patients, unconsciously at least.

Once these essential conditions are fulfilled, there can be no doubt of the value of co-operation, particularly in what has come to be known as psychosomatic illness.

A quotation from Dr Kenneth Appel, Head of the Department of Psychology in the University of Pennsylvania, on co-operation is impressive, coming as it does from such an authority. The passage reads—'A brief working knowledge of psychiatry is indispensable to the clergyman. He will understand more adequately the many motivating forces of human be-

haviour, the factors responsible for social effectiveness, delinquency, neurosis and psychosis. He will understand the guidance needed in the relief of suffering, and in the corrections of
deviations and ineffectiveness. He will broaden his view of man
and human relationships, and deepen his well-spring of compassion, benevolence and wisdom. He will become a better
family counsellor, and in this way, share in preventative work
of community education on mental health and illness. He
should in certain instances be able to help the psychiatrist in
his work with the most neglected people in our society, the
mentally ill. He in turn could hope to get more help from the
psychiatrist in community activity, group work, community
education, and social psychiatry, and persuade him to be less
preoccupied with the individual patient. Together psychiatrist
and clergyman could look towards the building of sound communities. Collaboration would increase the effectiveness of
each in his chosen profession, without the one usurping the
function of the other or displacing him.'

We have stated that, until recently, co-operation between
psychiatrists and ministers in the work of healing has been
largely sporadic, and has been confined to isolated areas. The
present generation of medical practitioners, however, knows
that interest in spiritual healing had become so strong and
widespread that the British Medical Association appointed a
Commission to investigate the claims of faith-healers, and
assess the effectiveness of spiritual factors in healing. A report
presenting the findings of the Commission was published in
1956. The enquiry was concerned, of course, with forms of
healing which completely ignored scientific medicine, and,
indeed, often condemned medicine and surgery as 'unspiritual',
and contrary to the will of Christ. The report acknowledged
the value of spiritual factors in the cure, particularly of certain
forms of illness, while at the same time it stressed the dangers of
unauthorized attempts to heal all manner of sickness by spiritual
measures alone.

What is not so well known, even amongst present-day
medical practitioners, is that at the dawn of this century, so
alarmed was the profession generally at the rapid spread of
healing movements, that a serious investigation into the principles and methods employed was carried out. As a result, the

British Medical Journal of June 1910 was wholly devoted to the subject. Amongst the contributors were such notable physicians as Lord Albutt, Professor of Medicine in the University of Cambridge, Sir Henry Morris, ex-President of the Royal College of Surgeons, Dr H. T. Butlin, President-Elect of the British Medical Association, and Sir William Osler, Professor of Medicine in the University of Oxford.

The healing movements of the time which were causing serious concern in medical quarters were those of Lourdes and Christian Science, although numerous less-known healing sects were making serious inroads into the membership of the ordinary Churches, and, indeed, were drawing away patients from the care of their doctors. The astounding claims regarding the 'cure' of numerous patients declared incurable by their doctors, provoked the investigation which the medical profession then undertook. About these movements and the claims of faith healers in general, the *British Medical Journal* had some penetrating criticisms to make. For example, writing about the claims of Christian Science, Lord Albutt said, 'Deeply as we sympathise with the hearts that will not attribute to God acts or implications which revolt our highest ethical instincts, which cannot see in the earthquake infinite love, this denial of the plainest facts of life is too audacious an imagination to serve us in the interpretation of disease. This is not to hope beyond knowledge but to defy knowledge, and the humblest truth must go beyond the noblest lie. When we refuse to face facts all is lost; we may not hypnotise ourselves.' The theory he is attacking, of course, is the Christian Science insistence that pain and sin have no objective reality. They are simply 'errors of mortal mind'.

Dr Morris presents in the same *Journal* an exhaustive analysis of the happenings at Lourdes, pointing out that there had been other shrines commemorating similar alleged apparitions of the Virgin, but these 'received their death-blow once Lourdes came into prominence'. Also that with the coming of a more sophisticated type of pilgrim to Lourdes the number of alleged miracles fell off considerably. In fact few now take place in any single year that cannot be easily accounted for as cases of mistaken diagnosis, or of 'instantaneous healings' that have nothing to do with the supernatural, or as effects of suggestion. Dr Morris cites many instances of 'cures' by 'mental suggestion' which he himself had witnessed, and which were just as impressive as those of Lourdes. 'But,' he adds, 'with the rise and fall of belief in the Immaculate Conception rose and fell the number of miracle cures.'

But another movement of the time impressed more favourably the minds of these medical investigators. It was the Emmanuel Movement inaugurated by two scholarly Boston clergymen, Doctors Elwood Worcester and Samuel McComb. On this movement Sir William Osler comments most favourably. 'The Emmanuel Movement,' he says, 'makes use of both the social uplift and the individual direction. Services of worship are held each week in which an address is given bearing directly on the afflictions of those present in such a way as to stimulate the proper attitude towards them. The mass effect of these services is prophylactic, often resulting in relief from minor ailments. Yet it is the clinic in which treatment is direct and definite. Every applicant must first submit to diagnosis. If organic trouble is disclosed he is not accepted as a patient. If the disease appears to be simple the applicant is registered for treatment. Where more is needed than full self-revelation—in itself curative—and the prayer and Godly counselling which succeed it, the patient is invited to be seated in a reclining chair, taught to relax all his muscles, calmed by soothing words, and, in a state of physical relaxation and mental quiet, the unwholesome thoughts and the untoward symptoms are dislodged from his consciousness, and in their place are sown the seeds of more health-giving thoughts and better habits. The spiritual result of such an experience outbulks all else.'

Sir William Osler concludes his favourable references to this movement by stating: 'The class organization, the association with church services, and the confidence inspired by the co-operation of doctor and pastor have been favourable features. It is impossible to say what the future has in store, but here is an honest attempt to bring back that angelic conjunction of physic with divinity . . . I feel that our attitude as a profession must not be hostile. . . . The angel of Bethesda is at the pool—we must step in.'

We may not be aware of it, but it is to this movement, headed by Doctors Worcester and McComb, that the

B

beginnings of co-operation between the forces of medicine and religion in the modern age owes its inspiration. We need not point out, however, how very different this movement was from those faith-healing campaigns that do so much harm in exploiting the morbid emotions, and also the pockets, of the unsuspicious, and are largely conducted by people who are familiar with the techniques of mass suggestion, but are quite unaware of the nature of those mental mechanisms which the skilled psychiatrist can use, without risk, in the healing of the mind.

Yet another factor influencing the minds of both doctors and ministers, so that at least they become willing to discuss together the needs of the sick, is a better understanding of the details of Christ's healing ministry. For one thing, there is no evidence that He consistently made use of any stereotyped methods of healing such as we associate with peripatetic healers today. These show no interest in the matter of diagnosis. They claim, as did the early defenders of Lourdes, that our Lord (or the Blessed Virgin) can cure any type of sickness irrespective of the nature of the symptoms. There is, indeed, evidence that He anticipated much that is viewed as important in modern psychiatric methods of healing. For example, He related the symptoms of the 'paralytic' (Matthew 9²) to its cause in a guilty conscience, and treated the patient accordingly. He did not lay hands on him, or simply admonish him to exercise faith. He rather applied the principle now spoken of as 'depth psychology'. At least our Lord's treatment of the patient afflicted with functional paralysis was along the lines with which psychiatry in our time has made us familiar. Many modern spiritual healers—especially those who belong to healing sects—always attempt to heal by methods of exorcism, no matter what the nature of the illness may be. Jesus selected the mode according to the nature of the symptoms, and in regard to their meaning He seemed to have perfect insight.

The story of The Good Samaritan has also much to teach in this connexion. This benefactor was commended by Christ not because he had ordered the wounded man to exercise faith, but rather on the ground that he made use of the best 'medical' methods known in his day. Thus he bound up the wound, having poured in oil and wine for purposes of cleansing and healing; he improvised the only kind of ambulance available; he had the patient taken at once to a rest-centre, and arranged that there he should have suitable nursing; for, of course, the nursing of a patient is almost as important a factor in healing as are the skill and medicine of the doctor. Furthermore, what was even more important than all this, was the way in which the Good Samaritan set the mind of the patient at ease, so far as hospital charges and doctors' fees were concerned. Anxiety over such matters can seriously hinder or even prevent recovery. Indeed, some forms of illness (duodenal ulcers, for example) can be induced through financial anxieties. Thus Jesus represented the Good Samaritan as a person of psychological insight, who, knowing the extent of the man's need, undertook to discharge all liabilities, not only for the present but for the future. His reason for such commendation appears to arise from His realization of the importance of peace of mind as an aid to healing. Such a consideration suggests the advantages of the Welfare State with its system of socialized medicine. These advantages are not always appreciated. Indeed, they are sometimes wantonly abused; but of their value to the health of the community there can be no manner of doubt.

Another factor in connexion with New Testament teaching in relation to spiritual healing is that such healing must not be regarded as an end in itself, as so many modern faith-healers suppose. Rather were these miracles 'signs' of the Kingdom's presence and reality. 'If I by the finger of God cast out demons, then has the Kingdom of God come among you.' There is much evidence in the Gospel narratives that Jesus used the cures effected by Him to witness to the reality and love of God, and to His Presence among men as the Bearer of their afflictions. This, indeed, seems to have been the prime aim in His healing ministry.

Amongst the most potent of the spiritual factors in healing of all kinds is that of *faith*. We are accustomed to disquisitions regarding this by ministers and faith-healers, but not so often by members of the medical profession. Therefore a passage from Sir William Osler on the potency of faith in healing is worth quoting. This is what he says: 'Nothing is more wonderful than faith—the one great moving force which we can neither weigh in the balance nor test in the crucible. Intangible as ether, ineluctable as gravitation, the radium of the moral and mental spheres, mysterious, indefinable, known only by its effects, faith pours out an unfailing stream of energy while abating nor jot nor tittle of its potency.' Sir William is here stressing the value of faith on the lower level as something scarcely distinguishable from suggestion; but he acknowledges how much more potent is faith on the higher level—faith in God who is Himself the Giver of health. Of faith in this Christian sense let a modern psychiatrist comment. Dr J. H. Hadfield has stated in Streeter's *The Spirit*: 'I have attempted to cure nervous patients with suggestions of quietness and of confidence, but without success until I have linked these suggestions to that faith in the power of God which is the substance of the Christian's faith and hope.'

Prayer too, is now acknowledged by medical practitioners as well as by ministers to be a potent healing force. Both are agreed, however, that prayer is not magic; neither can it be made in any way a substitute for scientific medicine. The limitations of prayer must be fully acknowledged when it comes to healing. We must not expect it, says Lord Albutt, 'to mend a broken bone or heal a torn tissue or renovate a poisoned or withered film of brain.' He goes on, 'If we are to be careful not to act contrary to knowledge, we know, and must candidly say, that the physical life of a sick man depends, not upon prayer, but upon the timely arrival of the physician with his antidote. In bitter certainty we know that the mother who in the hour of crisis betakes herself only to prayer will lose the child which is spared to the prayerless mother, who had learned the path of infection and how to outwit it. And since we have discovered the paths of malaria, of yellow fever and of diphtheria, have we not learned also that to stay these plagues no pageantry nor humiliations will serve us, but to look to our serums and water-butts. By no invocations can we even think to reach and to purify the cradles of disease; yet in the sphere of prevention lies the future of medicine.'

The essential truth of this statement is obvious; but if we must not expect prayer to do what medicine or surgery is designed to do, neither must we discount its value as a therapeutic force, especially when linked to scientific medicine. It should be remembered, however, that sometimes the patient is in such a condition of mind and body that it is impossible for him to turn at all to God in prayer.

Two other spiritual factors are acknowledged, both by psychiatrists and ministers, to contribute helpfully to the healing of the sick. These are confession and forgiveness, and fundamental religious convictions or beliefs. The former of these will receive attention in a subsequent chapter. The latter is to be distinguished from faith, which is an attitude of mind and spirit rather than a system of ideas. All faith-healers stress the importance of faith; few doctors, and for that matter few ministers, are aware of the close connexion between belief and health. Let us therefore quote from two psychiatric authorities in support of this. One is Dr C. G. Jung, who in his *Modern Man In Search Of A Soul*, page 264, has this to say: 'Amongst all my patients in the second half of life—that is to say over thirty-five—there has not been one whose problem in the last resort was not that of finding a religious outlook on life. It is safe to say that every one of them fell ill because he had lost that which the living religions of every age have given to their followers, and none of them has been really healed who did not regain his religious outlook. This, of course, has nothing to do with a particular creed or membership of a church. . . . It is, indeed, high time for the clergyman and the psychotherapist to join forces to meet this great spiritual task.'

The other quotation is from a more modern psychiatrist still. In *Christian Essays in Psychiatry* Dr Stafford-Clark answers Freud's contention that religion is mere 'wish-fulfilment' by pointing out that 'the central idea in religion is not a projection of gratification, but a quest: a quest for the purpose of life, and for the individual's place in this purpose; a quest for a relationship in which men can give rather than receive. . . . Substitutes for a central awareness and acceptance of God, are disastrous illusions, as inevitably foredoomed to tragedy and failure as was the Tower of Babel. If God exists, there can be no substitute for him. If he does not, existence itself is without ultimate meaning' (pp. 15 and 18).

To all this should be added the fact that, as a preventative as well as a curative force, the actively religious and worshipping community has not received the attention it deserves. Is this why the incidence of nervous illness appears to be so much on the increase? In relation to the needs of the sick, we are not making use of the health-giving influences which a worshipping community can generate amongst its members. We look to the doctor, and perhaps to the minister, to provide the necessary therapy, whilst the rank and file of Church members represent an enormous potential of healing influence. Here is where supportive therapy at its best should be found. It is the Church as a whole, and not merely the ordained ministry, which should function in this way. This, indeed, is what the 'Priesthood Of All Believers' means. Let a neighbour, simply as a neighbour, pay a visit to a stricken family, and his thoughtfulness will be appreciated. Yet this will not have anything like the healing influence, or the spiritual significance, of a Church member who in his visits to those in need, represents his Church. He will convey, though he may not even mention religion, something of the sense of the Divine Presence. In this connexion one further quotation from Lord Albutt is worth making by way of conclusion: 'Of solace, of the calming of fret, of the gentle hand for the body and the gentle voice for the heart, few words are needed. By solace energy running to waste is spared. For his reflecting brain man must pay the cost. By reflection his pain is infinitely multiplied; we suffer ten times over; pain and sorrows are fanned by regrets and by forebodings, and to their inroads is added the weariness of inhibitory controls. Solace at any rate we shall be content to call humane therapeutics.'

TWO

The Psycho-neuroses

As indicated in the preceding chapter, doctors cannot be expected to welcome co-operation with ministers in caring for the sick unless they are much better equipped psychologically than they usually appear to be. So in the present and in subsequent chapters, some attempt will be made to outline the main symptoms of the common neuroses and of the psychoses. The former of these refers to nervous disorders; the latter to more serious forms of non-organic illness, usually described as 'mental derangement', or even more commonly called 'insanity'.

Since large numbers of those affected by symptoms of the former imagine that they are likely to end their days in a psychiatric hospital, and since both they and their relatives are usually ashamed to let it be generally known that they are being treated by a psychiatrist, the rôle of a psychologically well-equipped pastor is obviously most important. He can ease the mind of the psychoneurotic patient by assuring him that his condition is not so serious as to be incurable. He can also induce the relatives to adopt a more sensible attitude to illnesses of both types. No such sensitiveness obtains where illness is thought to be organic; and the reason why this is not so, in regard to mental illness, is due to a long history of ignorance respecting the origin of these disorders. Nor did obscurantist faith-healers help matters by attributing such illnesses to demon-possession.

It should be added that the last person to realize the seriousness of some mental symptoms, or other handicap, is the patient's own mother. She will, therefore, resist as long as possible the idea of calling in a consultant, or even her own doctor, in the hope that the 'phase' will pass without treatment of any kind. In situations of this nature, on many occasions we have had to urge parents to seek competent medical advice without delay. But if ministers themselves are as ignorant of these matters as most parents, then they are not likely to give such advice.

It was at a very early stage in my ministry that I became aware of the importance of psychological, as well as of theological training for the work of the Christian ministry. As an academic university subject the 'new psychology', as it was called, was only in its infancy, and I became fascinated with Freudianism. I devoured any books on the subject as they became available, and ordered from America the magazine known as the *Psychoanalytic Review*. I concentrated my attention on it for a couple of years as a subject for a doctorate taken by thesis. But the more insight I gained into its fundamental principles the more interested I became in it purely as a study that could throw much-needed light on behaviour problems. Thus I studied, and described in detail, the behaviour reactions of any people in the community who were regarded as mentally abnormal. I had access also, through some of my doctor friends, to mental hospitals, where I learned much regarding the wide diversity of types of mental patients. Many of these whose symptoms I studied were described in the thesis referred to, which later on was published.

It happened that the person to whom I gave particular attention, simply because he was the son of a most honoured member of my congregation, some time later took the life of another in an emotional crisis. The prison doctor who examined him had declared him mentally normal. There was little doubt in the minds of the broken-hearted parents that their son would pay the supreme penalty for his crime. They came at once to me with their problem. What a pastoral dilemma would have confronted me had I been wholly ignorant of the nature of the boy's symptoms and what they indicated. The fact is that I had previously described the symptoms and offered a diagnosis of his case which I used in my thesis to illustrate one form of psychotic illness. I asked the parents to take this book to the prison doctor. This they did, with the result that he reconsidered the case, and I was requested to appear as witness at the trial. The jury was impressed with the fact that the book in which the symptoms of this patient's illness were described had been written prior to the murder; and they brought in—much to the relief of the parents—a verdict of 'guilty but insane'.

This took place, of course, at a time when doctors themselves had little knowledge of modern psychiatric principles. They received just as little training in psychology or psychiatry in their university courses as ministers did in preparation for their pastoral responsibilities. Today it is otherwise, and in similar circumstances fully-qualified psychiatrists would be called in to examine the accused and give evidence at the trial. The minister's opinion, no matter how well qualified he may be, would not be accepted by a judge who, quite properly, would refer to him as an unqualified layman and dismiss his evidence as worthless. A jury, however, can see the relevance to the situation in which an alleged criminal had been described as a psychotic of a particular type before the crime was committed.

PSYCHO-NEUROSES AND PSYCHOSES

No minister who takes his pastoral responsibilities seriously should be ignorant of the broad *differences between a neurosis and a psychosis*. At the outset, however, it should be admitted that a sharp distinction between these—especially at the early stages of the illness—is by no means easy to make. Often what appear to be the symptoms of a neurosis turn out, in the light of their fuller development, to have been incipient psychotic symptoms. A useful diagnostic point was given to me on one occasion by a psychiatric friend. He said: 'If the neurotic symptoms remain without fundamental change for a considerable period then there is little danger that a more serious type of illness will emerge.' This I have found useful where a patient afflicted with nervous symptoms becomes acutely distressed through fear of having to spend the remainder of his or her life in a psychiatric hospital.

Modern psychology, of course, points out that the difference between normality—if such exists at all in any strict sense—and abnormality, is one of degree rather than of kind. Whilst this may have some force it is not difficult to distinguish between so-called normal individuals and those who are obviously abnormal. Just as we easily distinguish between darkness and light (although no one can indicate at what point the one turns into the other) so with the difference between normal and abnormal people. Indeed, large numbers are border-line cases; and such can fill a useful place in society, although by no means well adjusted to reality, in some respects.

Admitting such qualifications as we have made, it is, on the whole, not difficult to distinguish between the neurotic patient and one who is mentally deranged.

What, then, are the specific differences which psychiatry underlines? The answer is as follows: psychoneurotic patients maintain contact with their environment, so that the world in which they live is to them no different from that of normal people, though, as just indicated, adjustment to their attitude to their surroundings may, in some ways, be less perfect. On the other hand the psychotic lives in a world of his own creation. This is often a world of pure fantasy. He may, for example, believe that he is the most renowned violinist in existence. On one occasion I asked one who had been for years in a psychiatric hospital with this very delusion whether he ever entertained the patients in the hospital with his special musical talent. Scornfully he replied, 'I do not cast my pearls before swine.' The world in which this man lived was not the real world, for, actually, he had no special musical skills at all. No such fantasies are characteristic of psychoneurotic patients. Nor do these utilize to the same extent as psychotics do the mechanisms of regression and projection.

Furthermore, neurotic patients maintain rational insight, so that they know they are ill, or unhappy, and have not the freedom of movement which perfectly healthy people enjoy. They are not only aware of their real condition, but can discuss it intelligently with their minister or doctor, and are eager to co-operate in the treatment suggested. Psychotics lack insight. They are usually unaware of the seriousness of their condition. Many of them are quite happy, especially those afflicted with grandiose delusions. They will not co-operate with their doctor—at least not all of them—and hence they cannot be trusted to take the medicines prescribed by their physician. This is one reason why they cannot be discharged from hospital so long as these tendencies remain. Psychotics believe themselves to be well, and cannot understand why they are compelled to continue the prescribed medication. They not only regard themselves as being in excellent health but are rather suspicious of the mental balance of those around them, including nurses, chaplains, and even the doctors themselves. Thus two questions have to be carefully considered by the Mental Health Review Tribunal Panels now set up under the Mental Health Act to adjudicate on patients who suppose themselves to be wrongfully detained. These are: 1. Is the patient liable to endanger his own life? 2. Is he likely to be a danger to society?

The question of heredity is also a useful, though by no means an infallible, clue to the problem whether a particular patient is psychoneurotic or 'mental'. There is, of course, no family in which somewhere, and to some extent, there may not be found a history of mental illness. Yet the family as a whole may be perfectly sound mentally. The fact, however, that there is some history of psychotic illness in the family, is no justification for hasty conclusions regarding a patient who shows symptoms of nervous instability. Where, however, there is a history of gross mental disturbance in the present and past generations of relatives, this fact, when taken along with the nature of the symptoms themselves and their persistence, should be regarded as confirmatory of a serious prognosis.

In this connexion a word of caution to ministers may not be out of place. On no account should a minister undertake to label any form of mental illness, and for that matter he would be well advised not to pontificate in regard to the diagnosis of even a nervous condition. Particularly in connexion with mental illnesses proper, he had better leave matters of this kind to the doctor. Because the charge of libel can so easily be made on this and on other grounds against one who is not medically qualified, a short course of lectures on forensic medicine should be given to all students for the ministry by a member of the legal profession.

With this preamble indicating the broad differences between the two main forms of non-organic disorders, let us now illustrate the main symptoms of the chief common neuroses. In another chapter we shall explain in detail typical symptoms of the psychoses.

Anxiety States

This is probably the most common of all nervous conditions; and although it can be distressing enough for those affected, and for their relatives, it is, perhaps, the least serious of all neurotic states.

Anxiety is, of course, a universal experience. As Paul Tillich reminds us, the threat of 'non-being' is the source of considerable anxiety to most people, for, of course, human beings are creatures with imagination. Hence they can anticipate dangers of many kinds, as well as the threat of 'non-being'. This is called rational anxiety. There is, however, a type of anxiety much more serious than this, simply because the individual who suffers in this respect is unable to explain the causes of his persistent apprehensiveness. There is nothing of which he is aware in his environment to cause him mental strain, and yet he is always ill at ease, and his day-to-day activities are restricted in many ways. A minister who has the confidence of his people, and who is psychologically informed, can do much —simply by listening—to ease the tension in one distraught in this way. We shall have more to say in subsequent pages about the healing effect of listening; but ministers in whom anxious patients confide know how frequently such patients acknowledge the extent to which they have been helped merely by talking to one who understands. Indeed, by encouraging a troubled person to unburden her mind one may help her to discover for herself forgotten experiences which throw a flood of light on her particular problem.

But what are the main symptoms of anxiety neurosis?

These are usually divided into two types—psychological and physical. The core of both is morbid anxiety; but this finds expression not only in psychological symptoms but in organic discomforts and disabilities of various kinds. Morbid anxiety is general apprehensiveness or expectant dread, the meaning and cause of which are hidden from the patient himself. There is, of course, morbid anxiety to a marked degree in other conditions such as agitated melancholia; but the psychological symptoms of anxiety-states are quite distinctive. They consist in *phobias*, or false fears; the opposites, agoraphobia and claustrophobia, are the most dominant. Agoraphobia is the irrational fear of outdoor spaces. People affected in this way only feel secure within the confines of their own houses; and so during the acute stages of the illness they tend to make themselves virtual prisoners within their own homes, or will only venture out when accompanied by a relative or friend who understands. They can, however, travel by car. Some who were known to me in the days when motor cars were not as numerous as they are today, had to be driven to their work each morning by taxi, and home again in the same way when their day's work was ended—a rather expensive means of transit in days when salaries were modest. Claustrophobia—the fear of being shut in—can be just as distressing and inhibiting, for those afflicted in this way may not be able to travel alone by train or bus, and may find it almost impossible to even enter a lift. Others dread crowds and tend to panic when surrounded by people in a store. They cannot attend church unless they are permitted to sit beside the exit and are assured that the door can be easily opened. Morbid anxiety can also express itself as irrational fear of a disease, such as tuberculosis or cancer. When this is so, the amount of ensuing stress is far greater than if the fear had a rational basis. Even the tests carried out by doctors, who afterwards assure the patient that his anxiety is groundless, do not always solve his problem. One whose apprehensiveness had been concentrated in a dread of tuberculosis acknowledged to me, when she came along for help, that she had already visited several doctors that day. All of them had examined her and found her organically healthy; yet their assurance did not relieve her distress.

The somatic symptoms of anxiety-neurosis are very varied. They include rapid heart action, fatigue, loss of weight, sweating, tremor, fainting, vertigo, asthma, nausea, retching, vomiting, and many more, such as skin disorders of which the patient is ashamed.

All these are psychogenic in nature, often going back to childhood. In this connexion, most psychiatrists emphasize the importance of the sex factor, the conflicts in the main being due to the clash of desire and fear. Conflicts thus created may remain dormant for many years and only flare up in a time of general stress.

Modern psychiatry on the whole seems to be emphasizing the significance of recent or present difficulties, or conflicts, as the cause of anxiety neurosis rather than those which occurred in childhood. Our own experience is that both are involved, as is also a hypersensitive temperament; and all have to be taken into account in explaining the onset, and persistence, of these symptoms.

The same basic factors may express themselves in two other neuroses—hysteria and obsessions. To a consideration of these let us now turn.

Hysteria

The term hysteria was so called because of its supposed connexion with the *ustera* which was the Greek name for the womb. The disease so designated was, therefore, regarded as one from which only women suffered. It was thought to be the result of a 'slipped' or 'floating' womb. But the fact that men as well as women behaved hysterically at times quickly disposed of this naïve supposition. Then the disease was attributed generally to demon-possession; patients were sometimes brutally beaten and tortured so as to get the demoniac agencies exorcised in this way. In the modern period, however, a more scientific approach was made to an understanding of this widespread disorder. Thus Freud began his researches into psychiatry by a concentrated study of the symptoms of hysteria.

He came to the conclusion that the disease was an expression of repressed sexual urges and conflicts, going back to childhood days, and to the alleged sex relations between children and the parents of the opposite sex—boys having sexual fixations on the mother and a repressed jealousy and hatred of the father, with unconscious guilt thus created. Similarly, the girl's sex interest was directed to the father with like results. Further investigation necessitated a radical reappraisal of such a theory. Later, however, the Freudian account of child sexuality was, quite properly, questioned; and emphasis came to be placed more on present sexual frustrations than on those of childhood. Furthermore, it was seen that the sexual factor appeared to be quite irrelevant in accounting for this neurosis in many people. Today, as we have indicated, the majority of psychiatrists would admit that the factors which most often appear significant in the causation of hysteria are precisely those which cannot be ignored in accounting for the onset of the other forms of nervous illness.

Like anxiety states hysteria manifests itself in two distinct sets of symptoms—those which are psychological and those which affect bodily functioning. Corresponding to these, two forms of hysteria are recognized. One is called anxiety hysteria and the other conversion hysteria. Not all psychiatrists, however, rigidly adhere to this classification. Some, for example, insist that anxiety hysteria is only another form of anxiety neurosis. But the clinical picture which one of these presents is by no means identical with that shown by the other. This will become apparent when we describe in detail the symptoms of hysteria in both its forms; and it seems, therefore, less confusing to regard hysteria in each of its forms as a neurosis distinct from anxiety states. At the same time it has to be admitted that the word 'anxiety' seems out of place as a description of the psychological manifestations of hysteria, but the justification for its use is the belief that these mental symptoms replace the morbid anxiety that lies at the root of both hysteria and anxiety neurosis. In the present connexion this is what 'conversion' means.

There is one general difference between anxiety states and hysteria which ministers would do well to keep in mind: the fact that the former is a *resultant* illness in the sense that it is an expression of the conflicts and repressions already alluded to; whilst, although these also give rise to hysterical reactions, yet the symptoms of hysteria, whether psychological or somatic, are always *purposive*. That is to say‘ they serve certain ends regarded by the patient as of paramount importance, but which cannot be reached in any direct or more rational way.

We have referred to the fact that experiences which in one person result in anxiety neurosis in another produce the symptoms of hysteria, and in a third those of obsessional neurosis. But why, it may be asked, should the same factors not produce in all patients one particular type of neurosis? The answer to this is that temperamental differences have also to be taken into account. On these, too, depend the nature of the symptoms which develop from particular painful experiences. Some, for example, are *introverts*. These tend to develop anxiety neurosis if they become nervously ill at all; and it will be found that persons of this type are always inclined to blame themselves for whatever misfortune overtakes them, although it is obvious that at least part of the responsibility for their condition rests on others. Introverts are seldom quite fair to themselves.

Other people are constitutionally *extravert*. These will blame the environment, including other people, for their predicaments and failures. They constitute the arch-critics and complainers of society. Seldom will they assume personal responsibility when they themselves make mistakes. They make constant use, all through their lives, of the scapegoat mechanism; and seldom are they fair to others. If they break down nervously their illness is almost sure to take the form of hysteria. Crichton-Miller recognizes as the basis of obsessions a type of temperament which he calls 'repetitive'. We do not find this name in the classical lists of temperaments; yet there is no doubt that amongst the chief characteristics of obsessional patients is their repetitive behaviour. They are always happy when repeating the same activities in their daily business; but force them out of their groove, and they will go to pieces. This and other characteristics of obsessional people will be more fully explained and illustrated in the next section of this chapter.

The fact that hysteria is a purposive illness renders any cure much more difficult than is the case with anxiety states. Clearly, if the symptoms are solving a problem, albeit in a morbid manner, to the patient they are more precious than gold, even though to the ordinary observer they seem to have a disabling effect on the patient. He therefore hesitates to abandon them; and if the doctor succeeds in inhibiting any major symptom, another, equally valuable for this purpose, can quickly take its place. No wonder doctors tend to become impatient with the behaviour of all such types.

In addition to being extravert in temperament the hysterical subject is also highly suggestible. His mind always seems hospitable to suggestions made to him, especially if these are in line with the dominant trends and needs of his personality. This is why a hysterical person can be hypnotized more easily than others. Already to some extent he is a dissociated personality; and the hypnotic state is actually one of dissociation. The suggestibility of the hysteric also accounts for the wide variety of symptoms which the unconscious mind can create. One patient, for example, whom I have known for many years, always had a fresh problem for me when I called to see her (usually at her request). On each occasion when I left she was most lavish in her expressions of gratitude for the help received from our conversation. Indeed, if one did not understand the nature of this type of illness, one could easily be deceived by the way one is flattered by this type of patient. The minister, especially, becomes idealized in their minds; and one therefore has to be on one's guard against the possibility, in certain circumstances, of emotional transferences.

Reverting to the story of this particular patient, the discouraging fact was that although after each talk her distress seemed to be alleviated, yet on the next occasion on which I called other serious complications had arisen. From her notebook she was always able to produce a description of these other symptoms which, in her view, were more distressing than those formerly discussed and abandoned. To me it has been a matter of interest that the hysterical patient is more liable than any other type to preserve carefully in written form the various complaints or symptoms that have emerged since a previous interview. Like the game known as 'the man and his object', the hysteric is seldom without her notebook.

At length there came a stage in our efforts to help this particular patient in which I decided that I must become much more explicit, and even blunt, in our conversations, so I began to ply her with questions regarding the satisfaction she was deriving from her illness. This baffled her and caused her to answer with great confidence that she was suffering from illness and could not by any stretch of imagination be finding pleasure in such a condition. However, I continued to press for an answer to this question every time I visited her, and spent some time listening to her complaint. Finally, she became exasperated and impatiently pleaded with me not to ask this question again. 'It always makes me feel like screaming,' she interjected. However, at the time some faith-healing services were being held in one of the churches close to where she lived. A friend persuaded her to attend and to go forward for healing. When I asked what had happened she replied somewhat shyly: 'As I knelt before the communion rails waiting for the laying-on-of-hands a terrible fear seized me.' 'Tell me', I asked, 'about this fear. What was it like?' After a few moments' pause she confessed that there had come over her an 'awful fear' that she might experience healing. There was no difficulty

c

thereafter in making her see the purposive nature of her symptoms.

From my experience of pastoral work amongst hysterical patients I have learned to attach little importance to complaints made by them alleging cruelties at the hands of 'callous' relatives, as when, for example, one such patient (a chronic type who has now been for twenty years in a psychiatric hospital) informed me, with tears, that her mother frequently dragged her round the kitchen by the hair of her head. When I undertook to question her mother regarding this she became alarmed and pleaded with me not to do so at present, explaining that her mother was liable to 'pass out in a heart seizure' at any moment.

Nor should the pastor pay any serious attention to such a patient regarding the unseemly behaviour, or infidelity, of her husband, until the matters complained of have been thoroughly sifted. Usually, if there is any basis of truth in her allegations, she will hesitate to let the matter be widely known. She is likely to confide only in her pastor (if she has confidence in him) or in some trusted friends. She will be sensitive regarding the good name of her family. On the other hand, if she gives the widest possible publicity to the affair, and does so without having first discussed the matter with her husband, then it is most likely that she herself is the victim of a guilt complex which she is projecting on to her husband; for it will be some satisfaction to her to persuade herself that he is as culpable as she is—though of course she may be quite unaware of the motives and mechanisms involved in her charges.

We have explained that hysteria is characterized by both psychological and somatic symptoms. Let us now summarize these.

Anxiety Hysteria

The symptoms of this form of hysteria are quite varied. They include the following: frequent convulsive fits (usually theatrical), jealousy and rage, often mounting in intensity until there takes place a discharge of emotion in some irrational and impulsive action such as the flinging of objects through windows and the smashing of furniture. In such tantrums even bodily injury can be inflicted on close relatives. Screaming to create alarm, or hysterical weeping, followed often by outbursts of uncontrollable laughter, are further common reactions characteristic of this illness. A double attitude, called ambivalence, in which love and hatred are directed, either alternately or simultaneously, to a particular object or person, usually a relative, is also noticeable in these patients, who are also well-nigh incurably self-centred. Thus as you listen to a hysteric as she describes her various symptoms you recognize how completely oblivious she is to the needs of those around her; and even when you call attention to those infinitely more unfortunate than herself she will almost immediately switch her thoughts and yours back to her own imaginary grievances and discomforts. Self-depreciation is a further symptom of this illness, and there is an evident tendency to inflict pain on oneself, the motive being to secure sympathy. Occasionally this takes the form of actual bodily self-torture, as if one's own flesh has become the hated object. At other times fantasies of being beaten up (masochism) take place, or the patient will be discovered writing threatening letters to herself. Usually the attitudes and reactions of all hysterics is negative. What they have they do not want and what they want they never have. Thus they feel themselves to be completely blocked and frustrated. This is why they often indulge in frightening outbursts like the patient who kept banging her head against a wall in my study, very much as though demon-possessed.

Hysterics also make use of dramatic behaviour to gain their ends, as, for example, when one rushes towards a near-by river ostensibly to escape from life by suicide, but actually to compel her relatives to fuss over her in alarm. I have always advised relatives to take little notice of such behaviour. Indifference to her dramatic behaviour may provoke an outburst of rage; but it usually cures the particular symptom.

All hysterics are self-pitiers. The 'tear-bottle' is never far removed from where they are; and, like little children, they attempt to control their environment by the use of tears.

I have often advised the distracted relatives of a hysteric to become interested in the symptoms noted here, and to look out for them. Invariably I have found this to result in some improvement in relationships, the relative now being more interested and amused than provoked.

It should be added that hysterical emotionalism, can in certain circumstances be devastating, as witness the wild frenzy of the Beatle fans, or the behaviour of mobs when emotionally aroused. A quotation from E. Graham Howe's *Invisible Anatomy* is a vivid description of hysteria at the crowd level. 'Hysteria,' he says, 'is a mass reaction, "all or nothing", protopathic. Here energy is at the disposal of the least common denominator, instinctive, emotional, timeless, urgent, and inevitably destructive. Hysteria is by its nature, in one and all, a state of hyper-suggestibility. . . . Hysteria is catching and spreads like wild fire; mob rule is a destructive eruption of sub-human energy let loose, at the direction of the most unscrupulous, loudest leader of the low. Crowd hysteria is, therefore, the easiest prey of all unscrupulous demagogues, who have enough hysteria themselves to be able at will to sway others as with their emotional and unreasoned oratory. With untamed energies let loose, the behaviour of a mob can fall to the lowest levels of human conduct, expressing its will to wantonness by fire and its destructiveness in lynching and the like' (p. 227).

Crowd psychology also throws similar light on the behaviour of religious hysteria; a special chapter on 'The Neurotic Element in Religion' is included in this book. In this further notice will be taken of the irrationality of religious hysterical behaviour.

Conversion Hysteria

The purposive nature of hysteria is much more obvious in conversion hysteria than in anxiety hysteria. Since the symptoms are physical it is little wonder that relatives and friends believed the illness to be organic. In fact doctors themselves, especially in pre-Freudian days, so regarded it and treated the symptoms accordingly. But, as already explained, attempts to cure hysteria on the assumption that it is a somatic illness are always bound to be futile; for no sooner has one symptom of which the patient complains been inhibited than another equally disabling one takes its place.

Conversion symptoms are extremely varied. Amongst those that appear most frequently are the following: the feeling that one has developed a 'lump' in the throat. This may be an obsessional rather than a hysterical symptom in the strict sense; but a useful diagnostic clue, indicating to which of the two categories the symptom belongs, would be to discover whether or not the particular symptom has provided an effective solution to the patient's problem. Thus one man who had been the object of an unscrupulous blackmailing conspiracy had his mind successfully diverted from the humiliating situation in which he had found himself by the emergence of the 'lump' symptom which, incidentally, was a perfect symbol of his predicament. The real lump was, of course, in the mind and not in the throat. 'Organ jargon', as it is called, often helps to confirm the diagnosis of a symptom as non-organic, and at the same time it throws light on the precise nature of the problem which it is designed to solve. Thus the expression, 'I can't swallow that', is a piece of colloquialism which we use when we are smarting under some insult. So long as we are able to retain the experience in consciousness, and take action to have the stigma removed, no serious conversion symptom may develop. It is otherwise, however, when the offending experience is pushed down into the unconscious. Then bodily handicaps are likely to take the place of the tormenting memories. These latter are now forgotten and the mind becomes poised again; for it is much easier to tolerate a physical symptom than a shame-creating insult.

Other common hysterical symptoms of the conversion type are: gastric ulcers, heart palpitation, anaesthesia, 'pins and needles' all over the body, functional paralysis of a limb or organ of the body such as sight, hearing, or dumbness. All of these, and many other such symptoms have a psychogenic origin, and are serving some useful purpose in a morbid way. Thus, for example, a lady who always had a passion to become an artist, but who instead had been compelled by her parents to undertake routine office work, developed 'writer's cramp', the obvious purpose served by the symptom being to retire from office work, without 'losing face', and to find a position through which her creative gifts would find adequate expression. The disability provided the exact type of scapegoat which she needed to secure this end. In fact the unconscious mind is surprisingly adept in creating the most effective symptom for the solution of a particular problem; but the patient herself has no idea of the meaning of the disability. Such unconscious motivating may be further illustrated by the case of an officer of the

Air Force who during the last world war had been assigned the most dangerous task of patrolling the coasts of Norway in search of enemy ships. These, when sighted, he was ordered to attack with machine-gun fire. The resulting conflict, created by natural fear and the dread of being regarded as a coward, he found himself unable in a rational manner to resolve. So his unconscious mind presented him with a solution in the form of a 'paralysed' hand. A further symptom with an obvious purpose developed while he was on his way to the psychiatric clinic for examination. Suddenly he lost the power of speech, and could not, therefore, describe his condition; nor was he able to give the doctors any clue to the origin of the symptoms.

Is there any cure for hysteria? This is the question which will be presented to ministers who attempt pastoral and spiritual therapy amongst such patients. Conversion hysteria, of course, requires the expert help of the psychiatrist; but anxiety hysteria is a type of illness which the informed pastor can do much to alleviate. Three conditions of cure are important: (1) A thorough understanding of the nature of hysteria as a purposive illness, and a facing of the facts in regard to what the symptoms are doing in any particular situation. This will require infinite patience on the pastor's part. (2) The willingness of the patient to surrender her scapegoats and renounce her infantilism. (3) Having seen how self-centred she is, to help her to take a genuine interest in people in dire need, and to enter into some sphere of useful work for others. In the section on bereavement which will receive attention in a subsequent chapter, this last point will have fuller attention.

Obsessional Neurosis

The symptoms of obsessional neurosis are very varied, but they can be reduced to two main categories—compulsions and inhibitions. Many of these are so irrational and fantastic as to give rise to considerable anxiety in the patient's mind. Thus I have known some to be the subjects of such far-fetched compulsive thoughts and feelings that I have been apprehensive with regard to their mental health. For this reason it is important that ministers should themselves be able to recognize the main features of the picture which obsessional neurosis presents, and so relieve the minds of patients who imagine that their symptoms indicate the beginnings of insanity. There is, of course, no question of this, and ministers should give definite reassurance to anxious patients in regard to the nature of their illness. We stress this, although, as we have earlier indicated, sometimes —particularly in schizophrenia—obsessional elements are found mixed up with incipient symptoms of a more serious mental condition.

Compulsions

With regard to compulsions we have to distinguish between actions and other states of a compulsive kind such as thoughts, fears, and doubts. These latter are compulsive in the sense that they cannot be dismissed from the mind by any sheer effort of will.

Amongst compulsive *actions* none is more common than the hand-washing ritual which compels a person to remain in his bathroom for unbelievably long periods scrubbing his hands. Patients have shown me their hands all tender from prolonged washing; and yet, though the ritual causes pain, they cannot bring the process to an end until they have achieved a temporary feeling of cleanliness. A patient known to me made use of her medicine for this purpose. This is how she was being treated in a nursing home in the days when doctors were not as well trained in psychiatry as they are today. This woman acknowledged to me in confidence that the use of her medicines in this way had actually prevented her from committing suicide. Another patient informed me that she had to wash herself at least one hundred times each night in preparation for bed, and had also to cover the chair on which she placed her clothes with sheets of paper. Other patients tell of irresistible compulsions to touch various objects in their bedrooms before they could leave them each morning. Some have to carry out a similar ritual on their way to work, whilst others feel they must change the furniture in a room, or office, several times each day. Failure to do this, they feel, may have the gravest consequences. Anti-social and anti-religious acts can also have an obsessional basis.

Compulsive *thoughts* are likewise very varied. Thus one university student could not dismiss the idea of death from her mind. She called it 'a dirty trick'. The thought prevented her from sleeping, so she had to take strong sleeping pills to help her to get any rest. Another found it impossible to dissociate her mind from the thought of the suffering of animals and innocent people. This occupied her imagination to the exclusion of all else throughout the greater part of each day. She had finally to get rid of all means of communication with the outside world, such as radio, television, and even the daily papers, because these were the chief media through which such stories reached her.

Some compulsive thoughts are, in their form, sacrilegious. These are often the shape which a neurosis assumes in people who take religion seriously. They do not affect people who are religiously indifferent. Thus one—a most sincere and saintly Christian—was compelled to relinquish the habit of private devotions because, as she explained, 'every time I kneel in prayer, horrible thoughts connected with the sex life of our Lord force themselves into my mind and I feel utterly depraved'. Another such patient was horrified when during worship one Sunday morning the expression 'damn the Holy Spirit' kept repeating itself in her mind, and no effort of will could prevent it. A Roman Catholic woman, greatly devoted to her Church, found it impossible to resist the repetition of the expression 'Jesus, Mary, and Joseph are impure.' Allied to this is the use of 'vile' words to which only the most depraved could deliberately give expression.

It may be added that these obsessional thoughts apparently exist in 'families'. The minister who understands this, often surprises the patient who confides in him regarding some one symptom, by saying to her, 'Yes, I know; and you have other symptoms as well of which you cannot easily talk'. To inform the patient about these is helpful; since it strengthens her confidence in the minister, who seems to understand her problem perfectly and is not in the least degree shocked at the horrible thoughts and images which invade her mind.

Compulsive *fears* assume well-known patterns, so that they are easily distinguished from anxiety phobias. One of the most prevalent of these relates to the fear of having, unwittingly, injured someone or even of having been the cause of his death without knowing it. One such patient spent the greater part of a night going from hospital to hospital in a large city enquiring anxiously whether anyone had been brought in as the result of a motor accident. He had an uncanny feeling that an accident had taken place, and that somehow, without knowing it, he had been involved in it. Another who made considerable use of a bicycle in getting round, informed me that invariably he had to dismount from his bicycle and take a look back along the road or street which he had travelled to make sure that he had not collided with anyone and then callously ridden on, leaving his victim helpless and suffering on the road. A mother suffered intense mental agony by reason of a 'knife phobia'. She had persuaded her husband to store all such weapons away under lock and key so that any rash action on her part would be impossible. When this particular form of her phobia was thus checked another quickly took its place. This was a dread of compulsively flinging her children under the wheels of a passing train. One of the most fantastic of such compulsions was the dread which affected one patient of 'hiding people in the bodies of animals'. This she admitted could never really happen. She was quite aware of its absurdity which in itself revealed the fact that she was not a case of gross insanity, as many would have believed. She knew that it was only a distressing *feeling*, but she was unable to thrust it from her mind. Perhaps the fear of being 'contaminated' or of spreading contamination is amongst the most prevalent of these compulsive fears. These are most trying to the patient who believes that everything he touches becomes 'affected'. These in turn affect others who come in contact with them. Thus 'centres of contamination' multiply until the entire environment becomes polluted. There is, of course, no basis in reality for this phobia. It is simply a feeling from which the patient cannot disengage her mind by any mere effort of will.

Compulsive *doubts* also harass the minds of obsessional patients. In fact just as *morbid* anxiety is basic in anxiety states, so, it may be asserted, pathological doubt is the core of obsessional neurosis. Let us add a few typical expressions of this symptom. A medical doctor—himself a victim of this illness—was one of many who talked to me regarding this problem of irrational and morbid doubt. Thus every night before attempting to retire to bed he felt compelled to examine every water tap, electric switch, and gas-jet to make sure that each had been properly turned off. The same care had to be taken with the doors and windows of his home. His preoccupation with these details was not a matter of normal, rational carefulness; for the ritual had to be carried out at least a dozen times each night; and sometimes the compulsion—so far as the water taps were concerned—compelled him to hold a bowl under each tap in turn to satisfy his mind that he had actually turned the water off. Obsessional patients who work in offices and have responsibility for locking every document away at night go the rounds to make sure, just as often as my doctor friend did, that nothing has been inadvertently left lying about. A dentist told me of the hesitation, and even torture, she went through before extracting a tooth from a child or adult, fearing lest by mistake she might extract the wrong tooth. Most of her evenings were spent, she said, consulting the textbooks to reassure herself that she had carried out in detail the proper procedure. Whether a letter had been actually posted or unwittingly dropped behind the mail-box is yet another common form of pathological doubt. Ministers will find this disability taking at times a fantastic form, such as the lady's who brought her husband along to consult me with a view to dislodging from her mind the uneasy feeling that he was not her 'very own husband'. Incidentally, she brought him to me because many years earlier I had performed their marriage ceremony.

Ministers themselves will be familiar with other equally absurd expressions of pathological doubt.

Inhibitions

Obsessional inhibitions also express themselves in many ways. Thus there is the inability to wear particular garments more than once or twice, after which they have to be discarded, usually owing to the development of the 'microbe phobia'. For the same reason a patient may find herself unable to sit anywhere except in one chair in a room, all other places being contaminated, or microbe-infested. Inability to cook meals is also common, the person dreading that a poisonous element has inadvertently been mixed with the food. One woman confessed that she had to spend long periods boiling kettles of water with which to make tea; but invariably having done so she found herself seized with an uneasy feeling that somehow the water contained 'disease-carrying germs'. One man experienced the greatest difficulty in deciding on a name for his newly-born son. Lists of all possible names were prepared by him; and these he meticulously examined each evening to make sure that none of the names proposed, if adopted, would be 'detrimental to the future health and good fortune of the child'.

Two other characteristics of obsessional neurosis are common. The one is a tendency to dread and resist innovations of any kind; the other is the disposition to be over-scrupulous regarding matters of trifling significance.

Obsessional people tend to become 'groove-dwellers'. They find it difficult to vary their routine activities in the slightest manner. They must travel by the same bus to business, and always occupy the same seat in church; otherwise worship, for them, would be impossible. It is, however, in the matter of personal relationships that this groove-dwelling tendency can have serious consequences. Thus it may be possible for an obsessional person to become engaged, but impossible for her to go forward to the altar on her wedding day. If forced to do so the person gets into a panic and threatens to commit suicide. More commonly, obsessional people may decide to postpone their wedding and offer plausible reasons for doing so. This, however, is no solution, for the postponement will be repeated later. I have always found that an explanation regarding the nature of obsessions eases tension, and makes the marriage—usually a happy one—possible. I have also found it to be reassuring to the patient to be informed that once the step of marriage has been taken her conflict will end and that (so long as the marriage is a suitable one) the person, having emerged from the groove of 'single bliss' can be happier than ever in the new groove of married life.

Scrupulosity is a form of *diseased conscience*. It makes decisions on any issue difficult through a fear of making a mistake which would gravely affect the health and fortune of others; though how and why is not always very clear. To spend money on a well-earned holiday whilst others throughout the world are in dire need causes the person weeks of acute conflict. Such an attitude may not be entirely unhealthy; but when associated with many of the common pathological doubt symptoms one must fit it into the total pattern thus created. Scrupulosity in many is carried even to far more absurd extremes as, for example, when one who for many years had been employed by a city corporation suddenly realized one morning that he had been a few minutes late in arriving at his post. He felt that he had thus defrauded his employers of so much work and had been paid for work he had not done. Then his mind carried him back over the years; and he began to try to reckon up how many minutes he had been late for work throughout this long period. He could only think of this in terms of months—even years—so, conscience-stricken, he made confession to his employers and insisted on making restitution.

It will be noticed that the over-scrupulous individual usually worries over trifling sins—if they can be called sins at all—while on matters of much greater moment he may have no qualms whatsoever.

Can a minister render any relief to the minds of these patients? The answer is that he can if he has a fairly thorough understanding of the symptoms. (This, indeed, is why we have endeavoured to outline the general picture which these present.) Then, as earlier indicated, there are the same fundamental fears, guilt feelings and conflicts at the root of this neurosis which we found present in the other common neuroses. What makes the difference is a peculiarity of constitution, or of temperament. To discover the nature of these psychological irritants is a task for the psychiatrist—although the informed minister can do at least as much as a psychiatric social worker to provide the type of background experience from which such symptoms as we have described are liable to emerge. Another general fact to keep in mind is that most specific obsessional symptoms are symbols of, and substitutes for, the repressed complex or conflict. One or two illustrations may make the matter clear. Thus one patient who had an obsession for rearranging the furniture in her office almost hourly each day, to the curiosity and sometimes amusement of her colleagues, was discovered to be the victim of an acute guilt complex. This found apt symbolic expression in an obsessional preoccupation with putting her office matters in proper order. Really the disorder was internal—a moral disorder—not an external and physical one. Our next task was to discover what lay behind such an obsession, and our heart-to-heart conversation resulted in the confession of a relationship with another which was altogether contrary to what she knew to be right.

Another illustration of analytic procedure concerned the person who could not decide on a name for his child. We pressed him for a reason for this inhibition. Gradually the reason emerged in his own mind. It was a fear that when the boy grew up a letter to his father from a friend in whom he had confided regarding a particular moral difficulty might, through a confusion of names, be opened by the son who would then lose all respect for his father. Much more detail had to be called forth and connected with this basic fear, including a reassessment of the guilt-producing moral trends and episodes confessed. The result was a definite easing of tension and the removal of the particular inhibition of which for so long he had been a victim.

Short of analysis—which requires considerable time and patience—there is much that ministers can do to lift the burden of distress from the spirit of an obsessional patient. Thus he should explain that, whatever be the cause, the condition is one of illness and not of wickedness. If the person is afflicted with obsessional 'evil thoughts' he should likewise make it plain that these are symptoms and not sins. Had they been expressions of wickedness then they would have been welcomed by the person rather than resisted. The minister, moreover, should insist that these thoughts cannot be banished by any mere effort of will, and that the attempt to do so only increases their obsessional intensity. Once the patient understands that they are forms of neurosis and not either mental illness or moral depravity, and once he learns to live with them until their roots are laid bare by proper treatment, he will experience a considerable easing of tension and spiritual distress. Thus the patient already referred to who had been suffering intense agony because of a 'knife phobia' was able to display all her cutlery again once she understood the nature of her illness and how to cope with its symptoms. However, this superficial treatment, whilst easing tension and, indeed, suppressing a particular symptom, will not result in cure, and one may therefore expect that another symptom—equally distressing—will speedily replace the one inhibited.

Finally, it should be kept clearly in mind that usually the function of an obsessional symptom is so to preoccupy the mind that it cannot become aware of the real problem, although this is clearly symbolized in the nature of the dominant symptom.

THREE

The Problem of 'Nerves'

Many of those to whom we minister, particularly in their homes, complain of what they call 'nerves', and they make this the reason for absence from worship. They state that they become 'fidgety' and are so self-conscious and ill-at-ease that they often feel compelled to leave before the service has actually commenced. To do so, they admit, is always a devastating experience, and one that fills them with shame. Such are always inclined to regard their action in thus withdrawing prematurely from a service as one which is noticed and commented on by the congregation. As a matter of fact, however, usually very few pay anything more than passing attention to any worshipper who leaves before the service has begun, or during an act of worship. 'Nervy' people are always hyper-sensitive, and distressed regarding what construction others may place on their behaviour if it departs in the slightest degree from what is normal. In part this over-sensitiveness is due to the advice of some doctors to the effect that their condition is one which they alone can help, that 'it is up to themselves', and that they must 'pull themselves together'. 'Nerves', however, require some psychiatric help as well as ordinary medication administered by the general practitioner. This is necessary even if the person concerned manifests none of the typical symptoms of a specific neurosis.

Anyone afflicted with 'nerves' renders harmonious home, and, indeed, Church life impossible. One such individual may make life in a home extremely difficult; but if two—husband and wife, or two sisters, or other close relatives—are of this type, then perhaps the only satisfactory solution is for those affected to live apart. This cannot be done without misunderstanding by husband and wife, unless they decide on separation. I have known many close relatives who always 'get on each other's nerves' when living together, but who after arranging to live in separate homes felt themselves much more friendly, and thoroughly enjoyed visiting each other and even spending their holidays together. In his *Invisible Anatomy* Dr E. Graham Howe says: ' "Nerves" implies a breakdown of our capacity for relationships. That is to say, the nervous state is one in which, for some reason or another, relationship in certain conditions cannot be tolerated. There are, or seem to be, only two alternatives: One of us must go, to be dismissed immediately, out of relationship into an unrelated state. It is either *fight* and you must be destroyed; or *flight*, and I am not in your vicinity any more, which is as good as you don't exist for me, and so you cannot trouble me.'

Why are human beings so prone to develop 'nerves'? In answering this we have first of all to appreciate that this, as well as even more serious nervous and mental conditions, is part of the price we have to pay for being made in the 'image of God'. This means that we are endowed with reflective thought, memory, imagination, conscience, and spiritual sensitivity unknown amongst lower animals, except in a very rudimentary sense. But, although these are qualities that make human beings a 'little lower than the angels', and are sources of satisfaction such as mere animals can never experience, they are nevertheless prone to create discords and tensions of which animals know nothing. It is true of course that an animal, on occasion when face to face with danger, can develop something resembling hysteria, and thus cause a stampede which involves other animals; but no animal can anticipate death as human beings do; nor are they capable of imagining, as man does, disasters that actually seldom take place. The guilty conscience, too, as we shall see, can be a major factor in the creation of 'nerves'. No animal worries over past delinquencies as man does; thus our memories, as well as our consciences, help to account for the nervous tensions that are peculiar to the human species. Our Gospel of forgiveness is, therefore, particularly relevant to human need, and especially to one's nervous and spiritual health.

Admitting that 'nerves' are part of the price we pay for being human we have to ask, Why do some appear to suffer far more in this respect than others? In answering this we have to take into account not only differences which exist between man and beast, but also those that exist between one human being and another. Some seem to be 'nervy' by constitution. That is, they have a highly sensitive type of temperament, and this appears to run in families. Even their children, or grandchildren, 'get on their nerves'. Others seem to have inherited a tougher constitution. We all know, and sometimes envy, those who are described as being without 'a nerve in their bodies'. Actually there is no such thing as one person 'getting on the nerves' of another, or of a person not having a nerve in his body. These are figurative statements indicating, as already explained, a presence or absence of difficulties in personal relationships.

On official Church Boards representatives of both types are found and if the minister himself is of the 'nervy' type he cannot be expected to have the calming effect on other sensitive members that the more balanced and self-controlled minister is able to exercise. Therefore, to learn early in one's ministry to get a grip on one's nerves, and learn something of the secret of self-mastery is of the utmost importance in the smooth running of church activities.

Environment as well as heredity can play its part in the production of 'frayed nerves'. This condition can be easily traced to tensions in the home in which children have been brought up. 'Nerves' are infectious. Therefore, even the child who has no genetic handicap may, through parental disharmony and strained home atmosphere, manifest at an early stage the nervous patterns and reactions of the parents. We shall have more to say regarding this in the chapter on 'The Normal and the Problem Child'. Meanwhile it must be admitted that some are born with 'nerves' whilst others have their 'nerves' thrust upon them.

We must think, however, of the effect of the environment in a wider sense on nervous health. The fact cannot be ignored that there has been a sharp increase in the incidence of this condition in recent decades. We are living in an age of 'nerves'. This has a definite relation to the competitiveness of our time and to the perpetual state of feverishness in which people live. The Americans have coined an expression which suggests not only competitiveness and complexity but also the meaninglessness of many of the goals towards which people strive with might and main—goals such as those of material wealth, or

D

personal prestige and power. They say that 'we are all in the rat race'. This applies not merely to mature people who 'strain every nerve' to keep abreast of the Joneses in business, but also to the young people who become nervously exhausted through a constant whirl of excitement from which they find it impossible to escape—not even for normal rest. Hence the unprecedented demand of the present time amongst young people for 'purple hearts', and other stimulants to wakefulness. Sooner or later these are bound to react on their 'nerves', even if they have inherited a balanced nervous structure.

We have referred to the fact that ministers may themselves be the victims of 'nerves'. This is to be expected since they are so much in the public eye, and, indeed, their pulpit ministry alone can be a source of strain—unless they are sheer exhibitionists. Since people (quite unwarrantably) tend to lose confidence in a minister who is 'a bundle of nerves', as we say, it is important, as already suggested, that he should take seriously at an early stage in his ministry the cultivation of a placid bearing in all his relationships with his people, both official and otherwise. Whether or not he can achieve this will depend to some extent on the type of people that constitute his congregation, and, perhaps what is more important, whether his wife and family 'are with him' in his work. The over-conscientious minister may become so absorbed in his work as to seem neglectful of home and family. This can result in domestic disharmony, and can contribute seriously to nervous breakdown on the part of the minister.

When lecturing to medical students in a university in the United States, Sir William Osler urged every student and medical practitioner to maintain the virtue of 'imperturbability' and exercise this as they engaged in the treatment of their patients. This in itself, Sir William affirmed, has a healing effect. He defines imperturbability as 'coolness and presence of mind in all circumstances, calmness amid storm, clear judgement in moments of grave peril, immobility, impassiveness, or, to use an old and expressive term—phlegm. It is a quality most highly appreciated by the laity, though often misunderstood by them; and the physician who has the misfortune to be without it, who betrays indecision and worry, and who shows that he is flustered and flurried, loses rapidly the confidence of his patients.' Here is most certainly a word in season to ministers as well as to doctors.

According to another physician, already quoted, Dr E. Graham Howe, the lack of this quality is often due to nervous exhaustion. ' "Nervy" people', he says, 'cannot stop. They must be always on the go, in constant fuss to overcome the many dictates of their outer world. They are at it all the time, at constant loggerheads with life, in a state of peripheral excitement. The outside world absorbs their energies and will not let them rest. Their minds run on and on within their heads, as if literally in a whirl. Driven themselves, they drive others if they can. Irritated, they are irritable folk, exhausted they are restless still; nothing seems right and they find fault with everyone. It is sometimes true that they do get the work done, but at what a price of turmoil and frayed nerves.'

Other factors, as well as those of heredity, environment, and overwork must be taken into account in appreciating why some are afflicted in the way we have described. In experience the following stand out as important: *pride or egotism, an over-exacting super-ego* and strain arising from *a painful sense of inferiority*.

Pride is generally regarded as the parent of all sins. In its nature it is, as C. S. Lewis reminds us, *competitive*. A person, for example, is not necessarily proud because he has wealth or is in a position of influence, but rather because he has more wealth than all others in his community, or occupies a position which others covet. This attitude to life adds considerably to its frustrations and strain, as well as to questionable devices to surpass the Joneses. Thus 'nerves' in many people are due to the compulsion to live beyond their means, and this is an expression of pride. 'The humble,' wrote St Thomas, 'dwell in a multitude of peace.'

The second 'indo-psychic' cause of 'nerves' is an over-exacting super-ego. For all practical purposes this is the equivalent of a sensitive conscience, but its roots go back to parental threats and warnings. Thus it has been defined as 'the voice of the parents speaking in us'. This 'voice' is often heard in one's dreams with disturbing effect. It was so in the case of a lady who, over a period, managed to get only brief periods of sleep and that under the influence of sedatives. Not long after falling asleep she became the subject of dream imagery in the midst of which stood out a threatening eye. When asked for associations to this she confessed that it reminded her of her mother's eye when angry. This led to a conversation regarding the circumstances in which her mother usually flared into an angry mood with her. She only did so when the daughter was discovered indulging in a particular 'sinful' habit which, according to her mother, would result in disaster both here and hereafter. Unfortunately the particular habit had become one of her besetting 'sins' and, in the light of this, it was not difficult to see how aptly the threatening eye mobilized her punitive super-ego. Little wonder that she had become the victim of 'nerves'.

Acute inferiority feelings add enormously to life's tensions, and if these feelings get repressed and form themselves into a complex then they do the personality still more harm. Alfred Adler's psychology stresses the fact that this complex is the nuclear element in all neuroses. So far as our present subject is concerned the Adlerian teaching is important since it brings into the forefront the fact that the inferiority complex always activates the compensatory principle, and thus produces a variety of 'plus-gestures'. These act as defence mechanisms against self-revelation, so that a person can be the victim of inferiority and yet pose as one who has fantasies of superiority. Thus he may affect an assumed accent, dress in a striking manner, and in particular strive after goals which he is incapable of reaching. He is also likely to become self-centred and preoccupied with a sense of his own importance, or form delusions regarding his fitness to undertake responsibilities for which he is not suited. Thus from inferiority stems much strain and an inability ever to relax perfectly.

In any attempt to deal with one afflicted in the way we are suggesting, the first requirement of the minister is to help the person concerned to understand himself. He can do this by explaining what an inferiority complex means, and how it originates. He may discover a variety of causes for it which should be discussed. Of these any organic inferiority should be referred to, or any disability which prevented him from sharing in the normal activities of school life. For a child to have his personality submerged by an overbearing parent, or to be discouraged by constant criticism of his school results when he has been working to the maximum of his ability—all these are matters that contribute to the condition we are describing. Sometimes the unreasonable and ambitious parent is himself a victim of inferiority, which explains his insistence that his son should distinguish himself at school or afterwards in a variety of ways. If he cannot satisfactorily compensate for his own inferiority he may do so through the identification of his ego with that of his child. This is what the expression 'the undifferentiated ego', which one meets in psychology, means.

It only remains to be added that the feelings of inferiority, from which so many suffer, frequently bear no relation to the facts. For many such have been amongst the most successful and capable individuals we have known. Actually, they are superior to the general run of people, yet they seriously belittle themselves, or else, in the ways suggested, add enormously to the tensions of life by the adoption of over-compensatory attitudes. These disappear only when a more just estimate of themselves is appreciated and accepted by them.

There is a statement of Marcus Aurelius, the Stoic, quoted by Sir William Osler in his *Aequanimitas With Other Addresses*, p. 2, which sets before us an ideal psychologically impossible of attainment by those who are the victims of pride, unreasonable super-ego demands, or inferiority feelings. It forms a fitting conclusion to this chapter, and is an ideal which all ministers, as well as church members, would do well to keep in the forefront of their minds, although it is, for many, by no means easy to reach. It reads: 'Thou must be like a promontory of the sea against which, though the waves beat continually, yet it both itself stands, and about it are those swelling waves stilled and quieted.'

FOUR

The Neurotic Element in Religion

Freudian psychologists insist that all religion is illusory. Their theory is that it represents a projection of our infantile wishes and needs—and nothing more. This view, however, is presented in various ways. Thus David Forsyth, a Freudian, says in his *Psychology of Religion* (p. 169), 'The supernatural represents the persistence and elaboration of a tendency which is rooted in infancy. Religion in the fundamental and final aspect still reveals itself as a childish survival. Just as a little child projects its fantasies into the outside world, and never doubts that they have a being outside itself, so religion projects its fantasies of spirits and gods, without realizing the infantile error it is making. The whole world-wide business of gods—from savage to Christian—is an example of projection on a colossal scale.'

In *Totem and Tabu* Freud elaborates the view that religion is simply a reflection of the son-father relationship in which the son both honours and hates his father. In working out his theory he makes use of the myth of the youthful Oedipus who slew his father in order that he might marry his mother. The various emotions which we experience in the family situation are, according to Freud, precisely those which we experience in religion—a blending of mystery, fear, and love.

The Freudian understanding of the origin of religion is put in simpler terms in *The Future of an Illusion*. Here we are reminded that in infancy we found security and protection in the presence of the father, or father-substitute. As we grow up, however, this attitude of dependence must be outgrown; yet the need for security still persists. What happens, then, is that we project the father-image of infancy on to the canvas of the universe, thus creating for ourselves a picture of God as a 'Heavenly Father', who offers us all the protection which we derived in infancy from our earthly parent. The general effect of such a religious attitude, he alleges, is to keep us in a state of immaturity and dependence. Freud predicted, however, that in due course humanity will outgrow this phase, and that when this happens religion will have completely disappeared.

Three comments by way of criticism of the Freudian theory of the origin of religion seem apposite:

(1) It is based on man in his primordial state rather than on man as a mature and civilized being, and if anything at all comparable to the 'Oedipus complex' exists (and non-Freudians with few exceptions fail to take it seriously) it is due more to parental possessiveness (as when a father pairs off with his daughter and a mother with her son) than to infantile sexuality of the kind which Freud describes so seriously.

(2) Freud is, moreover, under a misapprehension regarding the nature and function of real religion. As Dr Stafford-Clark puts it in *Christian Essays in Psychiatry* (p. 15): 'It completely ignores the fact that the central idea in religion is not a projection of gratification but a quest; a quest for the purpose of life, and for the individual's place in this purpose; a quest for a relationship in which men can give rather than receive. Worship, not reward, is the consistent feature of all the great religions of the world.'

(3) Obviously Freud's theory of the origin of religion, and of its function, has itself a psychological origin. As is well known he was brought up a strict Jew, steeped in a religion which centred in the conception of God as the punitive Jehovah. To him, therefore, religion was one of intolerable dread, and the reaction for him, as for so many others in a similar situation, lay in the denial of the truth of all religion. Here another brief quotation from Dr Stafford-Clark is relevant: 'No one but a Jew with scores of generations of Old Testament religion behind him, could have perceived things as Freud did; a man steeped in the Jewish familial discipline, who was at the same time in bitter intellectual opposition to his religious traditions and bent on proving them mere illusions' (p. 49).

Whilst we reject the Freudian account of religion it has to be admitted that the religion of many—amongst them large numbers of Christians—bears all the marks of immaturity, subjectivism, and neuroticism, of which he and his school speak. There is no point in denying this. The facts are plain for all to see who have sufficient interest to visit the centres where sects of various brands meet for their religious activities. It is particularly prevalent amongst the smaller and more obscure sects, also among some who are described as 'mystics'. In his book, *Varieties of Religious Experience*, Professor William James had much to say regarding this type of religion. So had Dr William Sargant in his book *Battle for the Mind*. The latter's investigations among American eccentric sects brought him into contact with fantastic forms of religious neuroticism, such as are represented in the snake-handling cult, whose strange ceremonies can be witnessed in the United States, especially in the South. It falls outside the limits of our present focus further to consider such weird phenomena, since the communities in which most ministers work seldom witness religious behaviour quite so fantastic as that which Dr Sargant describes. The examples we shall cite, although witnessed in the United States, can be paralleled anywhere in meetings conducted by many such sects.

In one of these centres in a United States city, to which I was attracted by a large waving banner announcing a mission of 'evangelism and healing', I found the place almost electric with excitement. A muscular type of woman was directing the singing of choruses to the clapping of hands and the shouting of hallelujahs. She kept prancing from one side of the platform to the other, encouraging the audience to sing more loudly. The abnormal manifestations which followed as the meeting proceeded had all the characteristics, not of obsessional neurosis (with which Freud compares religion), but of hysteria in some of its forms. Thus, some present lapsed into a condition of jerks and jitters, and others began to dance around the room, keeping time with the rhythm of the tunes. These seemed to be in a trance state. Groans and other inarticulate sounds were emitted from several. These were explained as representing the pentecostal 'speaking with tongues'. Several appeared to be the subjects of catatonia, well known in certain types of schizophrenia. They stood in a rigid condition with arms raised above their heads. Others were seen to fall to the floor; and in a trance state began to roll from one end of the enclosure to the other. All these abnormal manifestations were supposed to be evidence of possession by the Holy Spirit.

The sermon, as well as the singing, seemed designed less to enlighten the people than to intensify the emotions of all present; for after every few perorations the speaker called on the audience to say 'Praise the Lord, Hallelujah'; and the sermon, like most in such gatherings, dealt in a no uncertain way with the hell in which the 'unsaved' would spend eternity. I could find no indication in such preaching of anything like a Christian image of God.

This service concluded with a 'healing' session in which several seriously ill people were wheeled forward. Several 'pastors' laid hands on the heads of these sick folk; and, simultaneously with an abrupt jerk (which caused some of the patients to shriek with pain), the devils were ordered to depart. There was no evidence that the devils had obliged them in any way; and one could see tears of despair rolling down the cheeks of some who were wheeled away exactly as they had come.

In another centre a different type of religious neuroticism was witnessed—less crude and excitable than the scene just described, but nevertheless plainly neurotic. Here the preacher was a woman of striking personality, whose fame had spread far and wide. The Sunday service which I attended was well-ordered and characterized throughout by a spirit of expectancy. At the same time subdued singing of simple hymns by a choir, wholly composed of young women dressed in white silk, had obviously the soothing effect which could lull a large audience of neurotics into a hypnoidal state in which the preacher could exercise complete power over them.

As the time of the service approached, the spirit of expectancy became noticeably more intense, and a spotlight was directed to the door through which the preacher usually entered. When she made her appearance the spotlight played above her head, like a brilliant halo, and accompanied her to her place on the platform. Robed in white satin she presented the appearance of an unusually impressive and overmastering personality.

Although I found it difficult not to become emotionally involved in the situation and so lose my own individuality, yet I was able to sense the presence of certain neurotic factors. Firstly, there was the sheer *exhibitionism* of the preacher, which in itself was a sign of neuroticism. Then one could not resist the impression that, so far as the rank and file of the audience was concerned, it was *this impressive woman*, rather than Christ, who had captured the central place in their consciousness and devotion. Thirdly, there was little doubt that the *sex factor* was playing a major rôle in the performance—for that indeed is what it appeared to be, rather than a service of worship. This factor, as we know, was made much of by Freud, who, in addition to the other emphases in his treatment of religion to which we have alluded, argued that the religious and sex emotions are very closely related. In support of this he cites the florid use of sexual symbolism in mystical religion, the fact that religious 'conversion' is most frequently an 'adolescent phenomenon'; that is, its onset and that of the emergence of sexual desire into consciousness usually occur at the same time. With regard to the scene just described this third impression was confirmed when one observed that the overwhelming majority of the audience consisted of men mostly in mid-life, whose morbidity was clearly noticeable in the expression on their faces. But the chief confirmation of the dominance of sexual interest in the emotions of those present came some days later when the papers carried sensational headlines announcing the mysterious disappearance of the preacher. It was only after several days that she was located in the Desert of Nevada with a male companion. The extraordinary thing was that when she returned there was no enquiry into what had happened, as there would have been had the person concerned been an ordained priest or minister. She was welcomed by larger audiences than ever—some unquestionably being present through sheer curiosity, but the majority no doubt because of their morbid rapport with her. Such a 'disappearing' episode, of course, would only serve to increase the morbid factor.

Before passing on it may be well to issue a warning regarding the danger of 'transference' on the part of frustrated and hysterical individual members of a congregation, on to their minister. This can happen whatever be his age or type of personality. Further comment on this danger will be called for when we come to the subject of pastoral counselling; for, of course, the subjects of such transferences will wish to have interviews as often as possible with the minister on all types of 'spiritual' problems.

Continuing to deal with religion in which hysteria is obviously involved, let us consider a very different manifestation of religious neuroticism. On one occasion when crossing the Atlantic I found amongst my table companions two learned and devoted Roman Catholics. These informed me that they were on their way to Rome and were looking forward to an audience with his Holiness the Pope, to whom they had an introduction. They admitted, however, that they were even more excited at the prospect of seeing an Italian saint. Although I was dressed in attire suitable for Protestant clergymen they had regarded me as of their own religious persuasion. When on Friday at lunch time they had become disillusioned they became much less communicative. However, I invited them to tell me more about the 'saint' in whom they were interested. She turned out to be one in whose hands and feet the wound-prints of Christ crucified had appeared. These, for them, were the unmistakable signs of saintliness. As gently as possible I encouraged them to compare their image of a saint with that of the teaching of the New Testament. No such stigmata characterized the latter. We went on to discuss the chief differences between religious neuroticism and true saintliness—the latter reducing itself simply to Christlikeness of spirit and life. It was pointed out, of course, that the 'saint' whose stigmata had so impressed them could indeed be a real saint, devoted to Christ; but if so this was in spite of the stigmata and not because of them. It was further pointed out that none except those of strong hysterical temperament could develop such physical abnormalities, and that in such these could be produced under hypnotic suggestion.

As already indicated Freud believed that the neurotic element in religion was obsessional in its nature. That the religion of some is strongly obsessional may be seen by the following examples.

In the section on obsessional neurosis attention was called to the variety of symptoms which characterize this illness. Thus reference was made to the neurotic need for strict orderliness and regularity in one's day-to-day activities. Up to a point this is simply a matter of self-discipline, and is wholly commendable. But when it becomes an obsession which occupies the centre of attention at all times and which on the slightest deviation from the customary routine produces a condition of nervous upset, then it is a sign of illness. Furthermore, scrupulosity and the ritual of hand-washing to which earlier reference has been made may take a religious form. Thus we have known some worshippers who literally squirm if at any time in the order and form of worship there is the slightest deviation from the customary sequence. They feel quite as much upset by this as the obsessionalist who has to touch various objects in his bedroom before coming down to breakfast each morning, and who is miserable throughout the day unless he returns and performs meticulously his accustomed ritual. The same applies to the man who cannot walk along the pavement except beside the kerb, and who therefore must force anyone coming his way either to the right or to the left. Most ministers hear complaints about a member of their congregation who simply cannot sit in any corner of his church but one; and woe betide the visitor who has occupied his seat before he arrives. This type has to be understood rather than disciplined.

Slight obsessional tendencies affect a surprisingly large number of people; and these will find themselves much more at home in a highly ritualistic type of service than in one in which the order of worship is more flexible.

Scrupulosity is a common obsessional feature of the religion of many people. Letters galore come from them to their minister regarding all sorts of 'problems' which, to the normal person, are mere trifles. Thus they may wish to know if it is right for them to take a holiday, and so spend money on themselves while millions in other lands are starving. These also belong to the type that will be most scrupulous regarding the details of religious observances. Priests or ministers, for example, may have scruples attached to the administration of Communion—dreading lest a slight particle of the elements may become desecrated by falling on to the floor or lodging under the fingernail. Roman and High Church Christians also will worry over the danger of making a wrong confession, or conveying to their priest a false impression by the choice of words used; thus they will return again and again to confess the same 'sin'. Protestant obsessionalists also worry regarding participation in the Holy Communion—not through the fear of desecrating the elements, but because they realize the possibility of partaking these 'unworthily'.

Attention may now be called to two special characteristics of obsessional religion. The first is that this type of religion, so far from creating harmony, or wholeness in the personality, adds to the strain of life. This is due to the fact that the person whose neurotic religion takes this turn is always in a fever lest somehow, consciously or unconsciously, he may make mistakes, the effects of which he exaggerates out of all proportion to their seriousness. I remember one whose religion was taken by him with the utmost earnestness; but he was always afraid of involving others inadvertently in some mistake which he might commit. Thus he explained that frequently after ringing the doorbell of a friend he was seized by a fear that, in answer to a question he might ask, his friend might tell a half-truth. This would have the effect of setting up a train of evil consequences which would ultimately change for the worse the entire universe. So having rung the bell he would panic and rush home. The second fact is that the obsessionalist is usually a solitary individual. The hysterical type, on the other hand (with the exception of those affected like the Italian 'saint') seems to require the company of others before experiencing the emotions and excitability which for such is usually the essence of spirituality. Like the dervish prophets of the days of Saul and Samuel the 'ravings' or 'frenzy' (which the term prophecy originally connoted) could only be worked up when those concerned were banded together. This, of course, is characteristic of all manifestations of mass hysteria.

Although we have been mainly concerned throughout this chapter with neurotic expressions of religion it should not be forgotten that some types of religion suggest the presence of a strong psychotic element. This is serious, and the comment we would make regarding it here is that it is always due to the fact that already those so affected had been psychotic personalities. Psychotic religion, therefore, represents the replacement of dominant psychotic symptoms by those that are mainly the symptoms of abnormal religion. Thus the schizophrenic patient may thrust his head through a window, and explain that God had commanded him to do so as an atonement for his sins. The religious maniac may believe himself to be the 'Messiah', and behave as such, supposing that God had conferred on him some special supernatural gift which made him different from all others. Indeed, one known in the United States as 'Father Divine', who actually believed himself to be

God and had thousands of followers who shared his conviction, is expected by his deluded adherents to return to earth at any time. The melancholic, who as we shall see is also a psychotic patient, develops the delusion that he has committed an unforgiveable sin. When this happens his ego becomes completely engulfed in pathological guilt—guilt, that is, which has no rational explanation in any sin committed. Milder forms of melancholia can manifest themselves as religious neuroticism. Persons of this type will usually swell the ranks of the 'pessimistic sects'. These suppose that the whole world is corrupt, and that since there is no hope for its redemption God will destroy it suddenly by some catastrophic intervention. For these, as for the prophet Amos, the 'Day Of The Lord' is one of darkness and not light. They fix the date of the end in the immediate future, but no matter how frequently they have been deluded they maintain their belief, and fix another date quite complacently.

Let us now proceed to indicate some of the obvious respects in which abnormal types of religion differ from the essential spirit and characteristics of mature Christian experience.

(1) Neurotic religion overvalues emotional intensity in religion. This, indeed, appears to them the only element that matters, and the techniques used seem designed especially to produce emotional tension and excitability for *their own sake*. Emotion is, of course, an element in true religion but so is every other human function. For Christians religion means loving the Lord with all one's mind and will as well as with one's emotions.

(2) Neurotic religion is self-centred, the individual testing the validity of religious experience by his subjective states. He is preoccupied with these rather than with God and His worship. Mature religion is characterized by a concern for others, more than for oneself. It always finds expression in a persistent outreach in service to all sorts and conditions of men and women in the community and far afield.

(3) The neurotically religious is fearful of any new approach to, or interpretation of truth. His mind is prejudiced and he adopts an unhealthy dogmatic attitude to traditional interpretations of fundamental beliefs. Not even the Holy Spirit can enlighten the minds of those who are blind dogmatists.

(4) Intolerance as well as prejudice is a characteristic of the religion of neurotics. Most ministers at times become perplexed and disturbed by the number of young people of the university type, as well as of older folk, who appear able to keep their general knowledge in one compartment of their minds and their theology in another. In the former a 'modernist' attitude finds expression, whilst in the latter is represented the most extreme form of obscurantism. We find, for one thing, that these are to some extent the subjects of obsessional trends and so are 'groove dwellers', fearful of anything new. We recall the fact that Freud thought of all religion in terms of an obsessional neurosis. There is evidence that some types of neurotic religion, but not all, is best interpreted and understood in this way.

(5) The *'holier than thou' attitude* is a further well-known mark of religious neuroticism. We hear much in these days of 'exclusives' who feel themselves to be so spiritually superior to others that they cannot sit down to a meal even with close blood relations, and who as a consequence succeed in disrupting the harmony of family life. These do not seem to be impressed with the fact that Christ ate and drank with publicans and sinners, and poured scorn on the self-righteous pharisees of His day. Humility, on the other hand, is one of the chief virtues of a genuine Christian disciple.

An element of this same exclusiveness can be found amongst the major Churches. It is one of the non-theological barriers to Church union, and until claims to be 'the true Church', or 'the only Church' are set aside all 'conversations' on this matter are bound to be futile.

(6) Neurotic religion attaches supreme importance to *abnormal psychical and physical phenomena*. Healing through faith, for example, is regarded as 'divine' whereas the astounding cures that are of daily occurrence in hospitals are discounted as 'secular' and 'material'. 'Speaking with tongues', and the onset of trance states are the authentic signs of spirit possession, whilst little attention is given to the biblical emphasis on the 'fruits of the Spirit' in Christian character, and Christlikeness of spirit. The stigmata alleged as the proof of saintliness is an illustration of this misconception. So are the eccentricities of St Francis or of Francis Xavier. Eccentricity and neuroticism must not be confused with Christian saintliness.

(7) Neurotic religion sustains itself by *abstensions and asceticisms*. In it the 'withdrawal' tendencies so prevalent in nervous and mental illnesses of some types, are evident. This applies not merely to forms of classical mysticism and monasticism, but to many expressions of evangelical religion—particularly those that denounce innocent pleasures as wicked, and who exaggerate trifling 'conventional sins' into enormities whilst tolerating, and even practising the sins which Christ so often condemned.

Finally, it is necessary to raise the question why religious experience and behaviour in the case of some appear to manifest the main characteristics of neuroticism whilst the religious experience of others is obviously mature and integrating in its effects.

Amongst the answers which this question calls forth are the following:

1. Neurotic sects consist mainly of those who, prior to their 'conversion', are already to some extent disordered personalities, and whose religious experience—particularly under pressure techniques and with no adequate instruction in the Christian faith and life—was more of a psychological upheaval than a genuine work of grace.

2. Many so-called conversions represent a surrender of one's will to a sect rather than to Christ. Indeed, the surrender may be (unconsciously of course) to the person of the evangelist rather than to Christ, and in such circumstances if the evangelist is himself neurotic, which is by no means impossible, then his 'convert' is likely to be abnormal also. Indeed, we have known instances in which the evangelist became to his converts the chief object of worship. At least in one of the hysterically religious scenes described earlier in this chapter such was obviously the situation.

3. Some conversion experiences were motivated by purely selfish ends. For example, we have known these to take place to solve problems of domestic disharmony. Thus relatives who had been at loggerheads with each other over incompatibility in religious outlook have been able to establish happier relationships through the 'conversion' of one (usually the weaker) to the beliefs and attitudes of the other. But what a price has to be paid in all such circumstances in the damage done to one's personality, and in the neurotic type of religion which is so

produced. Some 'conversions' result in the *repression* of guilt rather than in its release through forgiveness. Perhaps too much is made of conversion in evangelical circles and not enough of forgiveness. The two do not necessarily coincide, though they should. Some who experience sudden 'conversion' know nothing of forgiveness as is evidenced by the fact that they seem to be more aware of guilt after 'conversion' than before it. Many, moreover, appeared to be better Christians prior to this experience, judged by the standard of Christlikeness, than after it; and let it not be forgotten that forgiveness rather than conversion is the New Testament word. We shall make further comments regarding forgiveness in the chapter on 'Confession, Penance, and Forgiveness'.

Some who take their religion seriously, and are, indeed, worthy to be counted amongst real saints, worry because they are the victims of neurotic symptoms. They feel that their phobias or other morbid conditions are quite incompatible with a genuine Christian faith. These should be reminded that Christians, like all others, suffer from physical illness from time to time, but they never question the validity of their Christian experience on this account. They realize—unless they are extreme in their views on 'faith healing'—that at times they need the help of medicine as well as Christian faith in the restoration of health. In the same way those afflicted with nervous symptoms need the insights of the psychiatrist before the exercise of their faith becomes wholly effective. Meantime they should not allow any doubts regarding their relationship with God to cloud their spirits, and their minister should reassure them in regard to this.

FIVE

Sin, Moral Disease, and Morbid Guilt

The purpose of adding a short chapter on this subject is to
indicate the importance of being able clearly to differentiate
between sin and moral disease, and also to recognize the fact
that many who feel desperately guilty, and who come to their
minister seeking relief and comfort, may actually be the most
saintly people in the church. In other words the difference between rational and morbid guilt must always be kept in mind
in pastoral practice. Otherwise, with the best intentions in the
world, the minister may be in danger of doing irreparable
damage to those who out of their deep sense of need seek his help.

SIN

A considerable amount of hard thinking regarding the subject
of sin needs to be done by church members who are capable of
doing so.

Far too often the word is used in sermons in such a loose way
that it may mean one thing to one listener and something quite
different to another. Most of those who attend worship will be
disposed to regard the preacher's remarks as dealing with some
blatant, external, immoral act; or more frequently one or
other of the so-called 'conventional' sins, usually condemned by
those who think that these, and these alone, comprise what is
really meant by sin. It is strange how many exaggerate trifling
misdeeds into major sins, and, indeed, furiously denounce
certain activities of a purely pleasant, and often recreational,
kind as though these were amongst the 'cardinal vices' which
our Lord condemned more than all others. It never occurs to
them, professing Christians though they are, that these conventional sins were never mentioned at all by Christ. Jung
suggests that the reason people condemn trivial 'sins' is in order
that they may cover up major ones. At any rate we may be
certain that when a particular activity which to the mature

mind is innocent and indeed beneficial to health of mind and
body, is condemned with obsessional force, there lurks in the
mind of the accuser far more guilt than he is aware of. To the
subject of unconscious guilt we will return later. In the meantime, however, let us add what has been written by a Christian
psychiatrist on this subject. Dr J. H. Hadfield writes in his
Psychology and Morals (p. 35): 'It is literally true that in judging
others we are trumpeting abroad our own secret sins. We
personalize our unrecognized failings, and hate in others the
sins to which we are secretly addicted. . . . Most of our emotions are directed against ourselves. We condemn the bigotry,
meanness, and cynicism of others only because we are potential
bigots, misers, and cynics. We cannot bear conceited people,
because we are conceited without knowing it. Allow any man
to give free vent to his feelings about others, and then you may
with perfect safety turn and say, ' "Thou art the man." '

Of course habits and activities which were thought at one
time to be harmless may be seen later on, in the light of fuller
knowledge, to present a genuine moral problem. The illustrations that come readily to mind in this connexion are such
indulgences as moderate drinking and smoking—the former, in
view of the menace of car accidents, and also on account of the
high percentage of those who begin as 'social drinkers', and who
never intend to be anything else, but turn out to be alcoholics.
More must be written about this in a later chapter. The latter
habit is now causing uneasiness, although formerly it was de-
nounced as sinful only by people regarded as religious cranks.
Large numbers of smokers are now finding it necessary to abandon this habit because it, too, has become to them what formerly
it was not—very much of a moral problem owing to its relation
to lung cancer. For statistics indicate that more than twenty
thousand persons died in Britain alone in 1964 from this disease.

The difference between sin, as the systematic theologian
views it, and the same subject in the hands of the moral theologian, is at this point worth a brief consideration, especially
because it is with the latter that the minister, as pastor, is
mainly concerned. The systematic theologian may fill many
pages with such aspects of the subject as the Origin of Sin, and
the meaning of the Fall, and in this connexion with the problem
as to whether there exists a personal Devil. He must give

attention to the subject of cosmic and social evil and the relation of sin to suffering. Moreover, he has to consider why God permits sin to exist at all; this will further raise the problem of determinism and free will. The meaning of Original Sin and its relation to Total Depravity will also call for consideration; and in his treatment of all these and other related themes, he will have to examine their history and development in the context of various theological traditions, as well as in biblical and extra-canonical Jewish and Christian literature.

All this constitutes a wide range of discussion; but the moral, as distinct from the systematic, theologian, is concerned with these subjects only indirectly, if at all. His main object is to show how sins, this sin and that, affect the lives of individual men and women in body, mind, and spirit. Thus moral theology usually presents lists of specific transgressions which it grades in their order of seriousness; and this it does mainly for purposes of confession and the spiritual discipline of penitents. It is to moral theology that we turn, for example, for a list of the 'cardinal vices' and for the equivalent virtues, as well as for an account of the difference between 'mortal' and 'venial' sins. This distinction is regarded as of particular importance in Roman Catholic moral theology.

In determining in what circumstance an act is sinful, and whether it is to be classified as 'mortal' or 'venial', the Roman Catholic depends on, and accepts—usually without question— the pronouncement of his spiritual adviser. Reformed moral theology, on the other hand, stresses the importance of paying attention to the verdict of one's own individual conscience. This, however, raises difficulties of its own, since consciences differ from individual to individual and from age to age. Thus what constitutes sin for one generation does not necessarily do so for the next.

Traditionally this difficulty did not appear insuperable to those who based their ethical ideas on biblical teaching. These regarded the moral standards of the Bible as absolute, and accepted them as representing the will of God. Furthermore, it was generally accepted that the teaching of Jesus—so far as its moral implications and demands are concerned—consisted in fundamental principles rather than in rules to regulate the details of life.

The appeal to Scripture, however, as a means of establishing, without doubt, absolute norms to which the individual conscience should conform may have satisfied older generations of Christians. Not so today to anything like the same degree. For one thing not all by any means accept the inerrancy of Scripture in every detail. Large numbers of the younger generation have no regard for the Bible as a moral guide book, and, indeed, they know little about it. How to convince these that morals are anything but relative, individualistic, and subjective is, indeed, a problem for the Church of our time. Many moral theologians are therefore casting about for some new and firm basis on which they can build an edifice of moral convictions, and in this connexion they are making much of the validity of Natural Law as a suitable foundation for the re-establishment of absolutes in morality. We shall be referring to this problem, particularly as it applies to the modern views regarding sex behaviour, later in this book. Meanwhile we have found, when dealing with those outside the Church who pour scorn on the old morality, that they are impressed when we show (1) that there is basic agreement amongst all serious thinkers regarding moral issues; (2) that the teaching of Jesus stresses the ethical *principles* that are generally admitted as valid by people of mature thought whether Christian or not; and (3) that these are such as are congruous with both Natural Law and experience itself *in the long run*.

Whatever conclusions may be reached, however, regarding the basis of authority in this matter, we will appreciate that the emphasis on the practical aspects of the doctrine of sin is carried much further in *pastoral psychology* than in either systematic or moral theology. For here is stressed the importance of getting to the origin of specific sins, especially if these are what we call 'besetting sins'. In this connexion new insights, provided as they are by the psychiatrist in his researches, are being used by the pastor to excellent effect. We know, of course, that the psychiatrist is concerned with the individual patient as well as with his particular symptoms, and he realizes that to get rid permanently of the symptoms a complete reorientation to environment is often necessary. In the same way, in pastoral work, the sick soul, as well as the sin committed by him, must be understood in the light of his upbringing, his domestic and social background, and his daily work. This, however, requires time and patience, and these, unfortunately, not every minister is prepared to give.

In my early ministry I became aware of the need to exercise patience in exploring the origins of people's behaviour if this was obviously wrong, and was getting others into trouble. Certainly one painful incident taught me the way in which interviews with those in trouble should *not* be made. On the occasion which I have in mind my superior asked me to accompany him to the home of a prominent member who, through an act of grave folly, had plunged the church into disgrace. The sin was of the kind which people at that time did not readily forgive, and this probably for the reason suggested by Dr Hadfield when he reminded us that we 'hate the sins to which we ourselves are addicted', in thought at least. This man was charged then and there with his offence, and was given no opportunity to say whether the charge was just or not; he was told forthwith that he must never again enter the church, and was ordered also to go and reside in another area of the city. There was, of course, no attempt to get to the background of the man's life in order to find out what factors may have led to his downfall, and no effort made to investigate his early upbringing. Following a most devastating castigation the man was left crushed, helpless, and hopeless. I can still see the utterly forlorn look on his face. As we left I could not help pondering over the question whether this was really the Christian way to deal with a fallen member. The words of the Apostle came into my mind: 'If any of you be overtaken in any fault ye which are spiritual restore such an one in the spirit of meekness, considering thyself lest thou also be tempted.' Restoration, not destruction, was surely always the aim of Christ in dealing even with the most depraved. Discipline of fallen and offending church members, of course, there must be; but the aim should always be the person's ultimate restoration and not his utter discomfiture.

Ministers can learn much from the methods practised years ago when every doctor was a 'family doctor' in the proper sense. That is to say, the doctor was guide, counsellor, and friend of the family to which a patient belonged. Such a relationship has not wholly disappeared; but with the best will in the world it is impossible in the present medical régime for any doctor to devote the time to each patient in the way in which the old-fashioned family doctor was able to do.

We wonder sometimes whether the ideal of the 'family pastor' is not also quickly disappearing; for, particularly in large city centres, the demands on his services are so great that he often gives the impression of haste, and cannot spare sufficient time to listen to people's worries, or to deal adequately with the faulty sentiments of those who give him and his people endless trouble.

MORAL DISEASE

From modern psychiatry we learn not only the importance of the individual as well as the particular behaviour which needs correction, but also the difference between *sin* and *moral disease*. Many ministers reject altogether such a distinction as providing a possible means of making excuses for grave acts of wrongdoing. It furnishes for transgressors, we are told, a useful scapegoat, and removes in this way all sense of personal responsibility for the sins they commit. They hold that so long as excuses are sought for, no genuine penitence, and therefore no real reformation of life and character can take place. Some sects, for example, are fond of distinguishing between themselves and the 'old Adam', or between themselves and their bodies, like the person who was indicted before a judge with a particular crime, and who blandly explained that it was his body, not himself, that was responsible. Whereupon the judge said, 'I cannot distinguish between you and your body; but I would ask you to accompany your body to prison for twelve months.' In principle there is no difference between the person who blames his body and the more sophisticated 'modern' who puts all the blame on the 'unconscious complex', and thus rationalizes away his sense of guilt.

While one has to beware of condoning a person's wrongdoing, one must at the same time take seriously the suggested distinction between sin and moral disease. Ministers in particular must be careful to do so; for otherwise they may wrongly accuse people and only make reform in their case more difficult than ever. To keep this distinction in mind we may again turn to

Dr Hadfield. In his *Psychology and Morals* (p. 48) he writes: 'The man who deliberately embezzles, gets drunk, gives way to his temper, or gratifies his passion, is in a different category from the kleptomaniac, the alcoholic, or the victim of perverted sexual or angry passion. As organic and nervous diseases have similar symptoms, and yet arise from quite different causes, so moral disease and sin may give rise to very similar conduct—stealing or lying—yet their origin is as different as in the other case. Perhaps the simplest case for illustration is that of the drunkard and the alcoholic; to the policeman and the magistrate both are "drunks", and must be punished. Yet the former may be drunk because of a depraved and brutish nature, whereas the latter may be drunk because of a nature so sensitive that it cannot bear the assaults of life. . . . The drunkard could stop drinking if he wanted to: there is no compulsion except that of deliberate choice. The alcoholic cannot; for his will is impotent to stand against the craving. The drunkard is deliberately sinning; the alcoholic is suffering from a moral disease.'

It is sometimes the duty of a minister to appear in court on behalf of a member of his congregation who has got himself into difficulty through an act over which he may have had no control. When circumstances make this clear beyond doubt then he should plead with the magistrate to recommend that the accused member be given psychiatric treatment rather than a period of imprisonment; for the latter is bound only to result in a further deterioration of the man's character.

MORBID GUILT

Closely related to the subject of moral disease is that of morbid guilt. Perhaps the most prevalent form of this is the upsurge of 'evil thoughts' which, as we have already noted, are symptoms of obsessional neurosis. This matter requires more than the passing comment it received in Chapter Two.

Since the 'sacrilegious' thoughts and 'obscene' pictures of which some obsessional patients complain are quite alien to the fundamental trends of the person's character, they cannot be regarded as in any real sense wicked. Sinful or impure thoughts in the proper sense are given expression through the characters of those who indulge in them. They deliberately

foster these and gloat over them. This is a very different attitude to that of the obsessional patient, to whom they appear so
dreadful that his entire being is in revolt against them. Yet the
more he struggles to get rid of them the more overpowering
they become. Some of those who consult their spiritual adviser
regarding these compulsive thoughts express concern that
prayer, no matter how prolonged or sincere, does not appear to
help. This serves to increase their sense of spiritual hopelessness, and causes the impression to settle on their minds that
God had completely forsaken them.

We shall see later on that melancholia patients are much
more likely to develop the delusion of having committed 'the
unpardonable sin' than obsessional sufferers, and since the
latter, in contrast to the former, lose all rational insight and
refuse co-operation with their medical adviser their condition is
much more serious.

The pastoral treatment of an obsessional patient with this as a
dominant symptom involves in the first place an explanation, in
the simplest possible terms, of what the unpardonable sin to
which Christ referred really means. Next it should be pointed
out that the problem is one of *illness* rather than one of wickedness, and that the patient should think of it in these terms.
Furthermore, the sufferer should be reminded that this particular obsession affects few who are not genuine Christians;
thus the obsessional patient, distraught in mind, should be
informed that the presence of this symptom is more a proof of
saintliness than of depravity. However, as in other forms of
nervous illness, the easing of the mind, so far as this particular
symptom is concerned, although this is a wonderful relief to the
patient, does not constitute a cure, and other forms of obsession,
therefore, are likely to develop until proper psychiatric treatment is provided. Thus the case already alluded to where one,
to her horror, found herself compulsorily repeating the expression 'damn the Holy Spirit' needed not only an explanation of
the meaning of her symptom, which—intelligent and co-
operative patient that she was—she readily accepted and
appreciated, but also several further talks in which she came to
see how much harm she had been doing to her personality by
treating her sex life as in itself wicked and to be rejected. It
was significant, in this connexion, that the unpardonable sin

obsession emerged in the way described shortly after her marriage. This person has ever since been able to live a normal and happy life, and is the mother of a delightful family.

Quite a different problem is presented both to the psychiatrist and the minister when the symptoms point to the presence of *repressed or unconscious guilt*. The ritual of hand-washing, for example, to which we have already alluded, is most likely to be evidence of the presence of guilt somewhere in the unconscious depths of the *psyche*. This particular form of compulsion is obviously a type of atoning ritual. The guilt, however, may arise purely from misunderstanding in regard to the nature of sexual desire. When this is repressed it represents, in the unconscious, a guilt factor. But more frequently, the psychiatrist or the skilled and informed pastor may be able to bring to light, and to link with the symptoms, some misdeed or guilt-creating traumatic experience, which, although long forgotten, has never ceased to create tensions, irritabilities, projections of guilt on to others, and in due course, the onset of the characteristic symptoms of a neurosis. There come to my mind two illustrations of this process. One was that of a lady who appeared to have all the reactions of a self-immolation complex. Thus she described situations in which she lay on her back beneath a high wall and with a long pole caused bricks to fall on her body. On other occasions she endured self-inflicted wounds induced with a piece of glass or a blunt knife. She explained that in this way she experienced amazing relief from guilt and tension, the origin of which she could not understand. The relief experienced in this way, however, was usually short-lived and so the compulsion had to be repeated over and over again. The history of her trouble went back to her schooldays. At that time she began to discover morbid satisfaction in writing to herself threatening letters, which purported to come from someone unknown to her. On one occasion a number of these letters was found in her room by her father who took them at once to the police. Investigation finally led to the discovery that the letters had been written and sent by herself. Her father, not understanding the morbid factor involved, severely punished the child. This led to the end of her letter-writing; but, as one would expect, this habit was replaced by the more serious symptoms which we have indicated. The fact is that when guilt becomes unconscious it always tends to set up a desire for punishment.

The root of the problem in the patient whose baffling behaviour we have described went back to an incident that happened repeatedly in her childhood days. This is how she wrote about it after relief through psychiatric treatment had been experienced: 'When the psychologist spoke of sex and expected me to talk of that, I felt as if he were trying to take out a tooth by hammering it. The very words gave me the creeps. During psychological treatment, however, a terrible shock, received when a small child, was brought to my mind and I was made honestly to face every detail of it. The memory of it terrifies me still, and I could not even speak of it just then, but later on, as treatment proceeded, I realized how this shock was responsible for my trouble, and how many other difficulties were connected with it. I could never have linked them up without psychological help. I felt guilty about that shock. I felt I ought to have told my parents about it, but I was afraid to, as I thought in my child's mind that what I was forced to do was a great big sin. Also I was told I would get a most horrible beating if I ever told anybody. So that incident, with all the fears connected with it, was completely forgotten. Now I realize that somewhere within my mind this feeling of guilt was at work. I had some vague idea that in suffering, in making a martyr of myself and depriving myself of life's ordinary joys and pleasures, I was atoning for the wrong. Hurting myself gave me what I can only describe as a sense of relief, but the relief was dearly bought, when the awful sense of having done wrong quickly followed, and in no time I felt the tension again and got relief in the same way. So things circled on. I tried everything possible to interest myself, but was haunted by what I had done, and what I knew I could not help doing again.'

Another sufferer afflicted also with a guilt complex explained that it took her hours to get through a meal, for she could eat only the tiniest morsels through fear of being choked. Her throat was X-rayed and thoroughly examined, but no obstruction was found. So the fact was that the 'lump' was in her mind, not in her throat; and this we have always found to be symbolic of some horrible experience impossible to 'swallow', as we say. With this clue in mind, the aim in treatment is to discover the original experience to which considerable shame and guilt are usually attached. It was only after half a dozen talks that the facts came to light as these were presented by the patient herself in the following unsolicited statement: 'When I was a tiny girl, as nearly as I can judge about a little under eight years, a man who was trusted by the family got me into a room by myself and absolutely broke through all the sense of modesty I had always had. While holding me to promise secrecy he filled me with fear, loathing, and a feeling of helplessness, and while I suppose he did not harm me physically as he might have done, he filled me with a sense of shame, and I suppose awakened the emotions which should not have been roused for years. I hated him near me and was filled with a nervous fear if I thought there was a chance of repetition. He was converted afterwards, and great was my relief to be let free to get the whole matter out of my mind. I was still absolutely innocent and stayed that way, absolutely free from any curiosity till a girl told me, when I was thirteen, the facts of life as told to her by a series of filthy-minded maids. Is it any wonder that I wanted to push it all away as something unclean? I had quite forgotten this until something I was reading in the book you lent me made it jump into my consciousness, and the feeling of sickness that came over me made me realize that it must be the thing that has been spoiling my life. I know if you are going to help me I must not hide things so I am typing this off to get my mind clean again. Even yet, it has power to make me squirm.'

Little more help, other than reassuring talks, was needed to set this person free from her symptoms. The 'abreaction' which accompanied the recovery of the painful memory set her free from the particular phobia that prevented her from enjoying any meal; and soon afterwards she was inviting friends to her home and table to show them how normal she had become.

This story illustrates clearly what the psychiatrist always bears in mind in his work, namely, that the symptoms of neuroses are often substitutes for guilt which has been repressed. The sense of guilt disappears from consciousness altogether and the patient becomes aware only of the fact that he is ill, but no longer that he is guilty.

We shall discuss later the bearing of confession and forgiveness on illnesses caused in this way.

SIX

The Psychoses

Already we have explained the chief differences between the neuroses and the psychoses, and have described the respects in which various neuroses differ from one another.

We turn now to a detailed consideration of the major psychotic forms of illness, and would begin by reminding ministers again that the treatment of this type of disorder, based, as it normally is, on organic or neurological factors, is wholly the concern of the qualified psychiatrist. The minister should confine himself to the pastoral care and spiritual needs of these patients, who for the most part are unable to co-operate even with their minister, and this chiefly because they have no insight into their needs.

The importance of having a fairly thorough knowledge of psychotic symptoms, however, is important in pastoral relationships, not only because this can help to make more effective the minister's visits to the home of a mental patient where relatives need the consolation and guidance which a well-informed minister can give, but also such knowledge of symptoms will prevent him from making serious mistakes. Some who possess a mere smattering of psychiatry are always, in their enthusiasm, in danger of attempting the treatment of psychotics. This is particularly likely to happen in conditions such as relate to melancholia patients who seem overwhelmed with a sense of guilt. We have known ministers in such circumstances to try to extract confessions of serious moral lapses from such patients, with the result that their last state was far more hopeless than the first. I recall also with what elation an inexperienced minister informed me of the success he was having with a 'paranoiac' patient whose dreams he had been analysing— much to the interest and relief of the patient. Little was he aware of the danger of even suggesting to a true case of paranoia that he needed treatment of any kind. This will become evident when we describe the characteristics of this psychosis.

Amongst the factors that constitute the basis of psychotic illness are: a family history of gross mental instability, some physiological defect in a member of a family otherwise mentally balanced and healthy, as, for example, a brain tumour, faulty liver functioning, toxic conditions brought about by the use of narcotics or 'the bottle', general physical deterioration brought about by advancing age. It is quite common, for example, to notice elderly people developing delusions of suspicion in regard to friends and neighbours who, they allege, have managed to supply themselves with keys by which the doors of the patient's home are opened, and plots laid to do them harm. This 'paranoid' factor is very prevalent in senile people, as those who serve on Mental Health Tribunal Panels know. It is also prevalent in many who are by no means elderly, and there is no major mental illness which assumes so many different forms and degrees of seriousness. Our first task in this chapter will be to enlarge on this, and we shall begin by a description of *paranoia* proper.

PARANOIA

There is no need to remind ministers that this term comes from two Greek words, *para,* meaning 'beside', and *nous* which means the 'mind'. So the paranoiac is a person who is literally 'beside himself'.

Paranoiacs are difficult to recognize, for outwardly they appear quite normal, and are usually amongst the most intelligent members of society. They may be found amongst the professions, or amongst the shrewdest representatives of the business world. They manage to conceal their abnormalities from their colleagues, and from the general public. Moreover, they can be amiable, gracious, obliging, and ingratiating members of society and, therefore, can be extremely popular in social life. To those who have to live with them, however, the picture they present is totally different from that which they present to the outside world. Thus to a wife and family they can be unbelievably sadistic, especially when under the influence of intoxicants. Indeed, as we shall see, life with a paranoiac can be a veritable hell on earth.

This psychosis consists of one central highly-organized

delusion of a persecutionary kind. So completely is it organized that almost everything that happens in the world can be conceived of as related to this major delusion, whilst all minor delusions follow quite logically from the major one whatever it may be. Sometimes the delusion becomes attached to a group such as the Freemasons, the Jews, the Communists, or the Roman Catholics. In these circumstances no particular member is in great jeopardy. If, however, as often happens, the supposed enemy is an individual, then the latter is in a perilous position indeed.

There are no half measures with a paranoiac. Should some person be regarded, rightly or wrongly, as having hostile intentions towards him, then he will begin to plot that individual's undoing, and will lay his plans so carefully that whatever crime he commits has little chance of being detected. Hence the frequency with which homicidal acts are reported in a particular community, but which remain a mystery so far as the identity of the attacker is concerned. Such murders are usually the work of paranoiacs.

Suspiciousness is one of the main symptoms of paranoia, and this can find expression in the most irrational ideas and charges in which quite innocent people become involved. Very often it is the man's own wife who is his greatest victim in this regard. Not infrequently will a paranoiac employ a private detective to follow the movements of his wife while he is at business and to report each evening if anything regarded as suspicious has been noticed. For example, all callers, casual or otherwise, are carefully scrutinized and descriptions of them preserved. Frequently also a patient of this type will induce one of his own children to snoop after his mother as she goes on her shopping errands; and if no detective, young or old, professional or otherwise, becomes available, then the time of her departure and return are carefully noted by him; and if she is later than he thinks she should be in returning home, she is subjected to a searching cross-examination regarding her whereabouts and any person with whom possibly she had been in conversation. If a paranoiac takes his wife to an entertainment, or to a restaurant or hotel for a meal, she must be very careful to avoid taking more than the merest glance at any male person in the place. A wife who is suspect in this way can scarcely attend her place of worship because there she will be in contact with church members of the opposite sex; and this can produce a fear in the paranoiac's mind that his wife may possibly form some clandestine friendship with a male member of the congregation. One such patient known to me went so far as to force his wife into a room and lock her there if he himself had to be away from home for some hours. In such circumstances it is little wonder that, sooner or later, separation of husband and wife becomes inevitable, and that the paranoiac ultimately has to enter a psychiatric hospital as a formal patient. If called upon, as he often is, to settle quarrels between a paranoiac and his wife, the minister's task is not an enviable one. The family will always range themselves on the side of their mother, knowing, as they must do, how irrational is the behaviour of the father, and how baseless are his accusations. The minister, however, is seldom asked by the patient himself for any assistance until his wife has deserted him. Then he may appear most penitent and promise to make amends. Should reconciliation occur it is likely to be only temporary; for any promises made by a paranoiac are quickly broken. Not infrequently a paranoiac will fasten his delusions on someone in the community in which he lives, and will bring the vilest of accusations against both his own wife and the man with whom she is supposed to be having an 'affair'. One such person believed that his wife and her alleged lover had devised between them an elaborate secret code in which certain ordinary movements or sounds were supposed to be media whereby special messages were conveyed daily from the one to the other. Thus the act of drawing aside the curtain in the home of the man under suspicion, the opening of the garage door, the hooting of the horn in the person's car, the barking of his dog and a variety of other normal, routine activities, each had in the mind of this paranoiac some sinister significance which his wife was alleged to understand. As a rule the first thing the man always did on returning from business was to examine the blotting pad in an effort to discover whether there could be traced on it any indications that his wife had been writing 'love letters' to her 'friend' in the park. Indeed one of these insanely suspicious individuals informed me, in the presence of his wife, that he had incontestable evidence of her infidelity from the laboratory analysis of stains which he had erased from the carpet in one of the rooms. Being myself dubious regarding his story I put the question to him whether he himself had not deliberately placed the particular stain where it was; for I knew that paranoiacs sometimes are more concerned to extract 'confessions' by any means from their wives than anything else. The fact is, however, that in most instances the wife does not even know the person with whom her name is associated; nor has she ever met him even casually.

The minister who may be called on to help where there is trouble between a paranoiac and his wife must be on his guard against saying anything about the mental condition of the man concerned. A paranoiac can easily take an action against one who makes any suggestion reflecting on his mental ill-health or character. Moreover, there is always the danger that the patient will now direct his delusion towards the minister himself; if he does, the situation will become perilous indeed for him.

The following story from my own experience will illustrate the kind of thing that can happen. When speaking at a 'Pastors' School' in the United States I happened to devote one lecture to an account of paranoia and its dangers. I had scarcely concluded my lecture when a minister and his wife rushed forward to ask whether I could provide them with a copy of my lecture. When I enquired why they wanted it they poured out their hearts to me. I could see that they were both under intense strain, the fact being that the pastor had become the victim of the vicious plotting of a paranoiac member of his congregation. Annoyance from him began after the pastor had threatened to institute disciplinary action against him as a trouble-maker in the congregation. This initiated a series of plots of the most diabolical kind against the pastor. His main purpose was to circulate rumours suggesting that the pastor had not a very honourable record so far as his relationships with women were concerned. He continued in a most cunning way to circulate these rumours throughout the congregation; and, human nature being the fallen thing that it is, people are ever ready to believe the worst rather than the best. Thus the story, or stories, so persistently renewed in different forms, were finally taken seriously and obtained publicity in the daily press.

F

Church authorities had now to take action; and in the trial of the minister one of the witnesses, supposed to be able to furnish first-hand information about the matter, was the very man who was responsible for the rumours. So skilfully had he marshalled his facts that it was difficult for any impartial tribunal not to be impressed. It was at this juncture that the 'Pastors' School' was in session, and the description I had given of the type and behaviour of paranoiacs threw much-needed light on the problem of this man's conduct.

I of course provided them with the substance of the lecture. This they brought not only to the tribunal but to the lawyer in charge of the case. The result was that the problem was now approached from a fresh angle; and finally the pastor was completely exonerated, and the paranoiac concerned exposed. Not only so, but investigation led to the discovery that this same man had been responsible for some diabolical crimes, in which he had managed to get his own wife involved, having first compelled her to write a confession, promising that if she did so no harm would come her way.

This story from my personal experience should make sufficiently plain how careful we have to be in our relationships with a paranoiac. We are not likely to know that such a dangerous individual is amongst our church members; but actually he may be in the inner circle of responsible office-bearers. It is likely that we shall be able to obtain possession of the facts only when his broken-hearted wife comes, in desperation, to unburden her mind to us. This is the point at which it may be advisable to consult not only a psychiatrist but also one's bishop, or one's superior in the ministry, or perhaps a small well-selected group of other ministers.

It should perhaps be added that seldom is a minister's help sought in dealing with a situation of this kind in which a female is involved as the paranoiac aggressor. Uusually the offender is of the male sex. This, at any rate, has been my own experience. However, large numbers of women, who cannot be classed as true paranoiacs (for the number of such even among men, is few) are to be found among those who manifest paranoid characteristics. The next section will take this into account.

SCHIZOPHRENIA

It was not until the beginning of the present century that a serious study of the illness now known as 'schizophrenia' was undertaken. Previously patients afflicted with this illness had little done for them, and the prognosis in their case was regarded as practically hopeless. Indeed, the name by which the illness was known—'adolescent insanity'—was in itself an indication of the lack of understanding of the nature of this illness, even among members of the medical profession.

The remarkable advances made in the understanding and treatment of the disease in the past half-century or more, is due in large measure to the pioneering work of two famous psychiatrists—Emil Kraepelin and Eugen Bleuler. The work of the former took place in the first decade of the century. It resulted in two main conclusions. One was that the onset of the illness always coincided with the beginnings of adolescence, and the other, that invariably the disease was characterized by a progressive deterioration of the personality in all its aspects, until a condition of almost complete disintegration had been reached. Accordingly, Kraepelin aptly named the disease 'dementia praecox'.

Bleuler, building on the researches of Kraepelin, saw that while in the main the latter's observations were correct, yet in some respects they needed modification. For example, he found that although the illness usually became serious in adolescence, there were many instances in which it did not appear—at least in any pronounced form—until much later. Moreover, he found that the deterioration of personality which is characteristic of this illness, was not so steady, gradual, or progressive, as Kraepelin had supposed. On the contrary, some patients, according to Bleuler's observations, experienced prolonged periods of remission, during which they appeared to have become quite normal; whilst others, after an initial acute attack, were known to have permanently regained normal health. I myself have been acquainted with more than one who for a time displayed the undoubted characteristic symptoms of this illness, but yet later achieved sufficient adjustment to reality to be able to live a fairly normal life and undertake important professional or business duties. One of these, whom I knew most intimately since his first serious breakdown as a sixth former in a grammar school, recovered sufficiently to be able to join the Royal Air Force in the early stages of the war. He became a successful pilot; though we have to add that he was tragically killed in action over Germany on the last day of hostilities.

As a result of his investigations Bleuler suggested that a more appropriate name for this illness—hitherto known as 'dementia praecox'—would be 'schizophrenia'. This comes from the Greek *schizo*, 'I split', and *phren*, meaning 'the diaphragm', which was supposed to be the organic basis of feeling or emotion. Thus schizophrenia is basically a condition of dissociation of personality, the dissociation affecting at first the feeling aspects of the self, but by no means being confined to this.

If dissociation is a basic factor in the understanding of schizophrenia, then since hysteria also indicates some degree of dissociation, what, it may be asked, is the difference between these two types of illness? Some psychiatrists, indeed, suggest that basically there is no real distinction between them; and they point to such hysterical symptoms as sleep-walking and automatic writing, multiple personality and strange phenomena such as are often witnessed in spiritualistic seances, as indicative of the extent to which hysterical subjects may be affected in this way. However, the differences between the clinical pictures of these two forms of illness are quite unmistakable. Thus the hysteric maintains his hold on reality to an extent impossible, as we shall see, in schizophrenia. Moreover, he does not completely lose insight into his own condition. Furthermore, the temperaments of both differ from each other—the hysteric being strongly extravert, manifesting a childish dependence on others, and seeking consolation from them. The schizophrenic, on the other hand, is strongly introverted and seeks consolation from no one. Furthermore, the illness of a hysteric is usually due to an unfavourable environment, whilst that of the schizophrenic is largely the result of an unhealthy heredity.

The fact that schizophrenics are seriously withdrawn from reality needs to be underlined if these patients are to be understood. As the illness develops, more and more contacts with real life seem to give way, compelling these patients to retreat to a world of their own making. As one listens and tries to understand them, one realizes how bizarre are their ideas compared with those of the hysteric. They attach most incongruous meanings to common objects, like the patient who several times in an interview called a chair a policeman, and made use of a variety of neologisms in the attempt to give expression to her strange thoughts and feelings. Such patients often manifest complete inability to appreciate the meaning of the questions put to them; and when they attempt to answer them they show how completely they have missed the point of the question.

These patients also manifest a considerable degree of what is called 'thought-blocking'. This means an inability to carry on a sustained and coherent conversation. They leave sentences half finished, remain silent for a few moments, and then resume conversation, or make remarks about something that has no connexion with what they had previously tried to say.

In his *Clinical Lectures on Psychological Medicine* Dr Henry Yellowlees has much to say regarding the extent to which the schizophrenic has retreated from reality into a world of his own. He compares this type of patient to a ship made secure in harbour by ropes fastened to the quay. So long as contact with the shore is maintained in this way the ship is not in peril; but let the ropes one by one give way, so that communication with the shore is interrupted, then, should the ship need attention inside or outside, repairs cannot be carried out. Moreover, the ship, very much at the mercy of storm and currents, is liable to drift; and the situation so far as its safety is concerned, becomes dangerous in the extreme. So it is with schizophrenic patients. Once all contact with reality has been broken then the prognosis, so far as these patients are concerned, becomes one of the greatest seriousness, although the outlook is not now regarded as quite so hopeless as formerly.

The withdrawal tendency in schizophrenia is further vividly illustrated by Dr Yellowlees in his book *Out of Working Hours*. Here he makes excellent use of the story of the Garden of Eden in throwing light on the characteristics and dangers of adolescence. The narrative indicates the stages through which children pass on the way to and during normal adolescence. The Garden itself represents happy childhood, secure from the dangers of the outside world, and perfectly innocent. Soon,

however, signs of maturing appear, such as a desire for knowledge. 'They saw that the tree was to be desired to make one
wise.' Then there is evidence of resistance to authority. 'Yea
hath God said ye shall not eat thereof?' This is followed by the
awakening of sex. 'They knew that they were naked, and they
went and hid themselves.' Finally, there emerges the impulse
to leave childhood behind and face life with all its hazards
and demands. It is true that the Garden story explains work
as a punishment for disobedience, and here the analogy between
the Eden episode and adolescence breaks down a little. What
matters, however, is that as adolescence develops, adjustments
have to be made to the life of reality and serious living. Now
not all can make this change easily. There is a small minority
of people who possess the schizophrenic temperament of over-
sensitiveness and timidity. These may shrink from adulthood
and cling with desperation to childhood. To do so, however,
they must develop the symptoms of an illness, and these often
take the form of schizophrenic fantasies and grandiose delusions.

Not all patients affected with this illness become hallucinated;
but it is possible for many to be victims after this fashion, though
not so overtly. One, for example, may overhear a schizophrenic
talking aloud, or even scolding. We say that he is talking to
himself; but as a matter of fact he may be addressing some
hallucinatory figure.

Hallucinations are either auditory or visual. Thus one
patient, who had a brother in the Royal Air Force during the
war years, believed that he heard his brother's voice sending
messages to him from every plane that flew overhead. He
heard voices but saw no one. Others see people but hear no
voices. One such patient complained that her bedroom became
crowded every night with 'visitors', many of whom she recognized as neighbours, who had recently died. They troubled
her only when the lights had been switched off. They disappeared suddenly when she turned the light on again; so, to
prevent this frightening experience from happening, her light
was kept on throughout the night. Yet another patient, with
whom I had an interview, and to whom I had just said 'Good-
bye', rushed back into my house in a panic. 'Come,' said he,
'and see these people in the hedge. They are making grimaces
at me.' Taking him by the arm I encouraged him to approach

them, assuring him that I would see that they would not harm him. As we came near the spot he said, 'They are not there now'; but then, on turning round to go back, he saw them squatting on the roof of an adjoining house.

Psychiatry distinguishes three types of schizophrenic illness —hebephrenic, catatonic, and paranoid forms. The first name comes from the Greek *hebes*, meaning youth or spring. This however, gives us no definite clue to what hebephrenic schizophrenia means. The word strictly means a condition of youth. However, psychiatry has enlarged the meaning of the term to indicate that this form of the illness develops earlier than either of the other two. In this respect the word *hebes* is not without significance. What is stressed, however, in any attempt to characterize this form of schizophrenia, is that not only is its onset noticeable early in adolescence, but that it is the affective side of the personality which at first appears seriously to be attacked. Thus patients of this type become unusually apathetic and depressed. They give expression to the most absurd ideas. Moreover, they become negative and uncooperative, and are most likely to experience the kind of 'thought-blocking' to which we have already referred. They tend to laugh hilariously in circumstances that depress a normal person, and to weep at the reception of gifts, or of any cheering news; so any attempts made by relatives to 'keep their spirits up' prove to be quite futile. These patients also tend to become slovenly, unclean, and untidy to an unusual degree. Catatonic schizophrenics present a very different picture. Patients of this type are likely to 'stay put' for a considerable time. With hands clasped above their head they may remain quite rigid for a long period. If asked for an explanation of this they may say that God had commanded them to maintain that position, and so they dare not do otherwise until God gives them permission to relax. Some get on all fours, and others may indulge in automatic mimicry. One may hear them, for example, imitating the bark of a dog or the call of some other animal.

The most characteristic feature of catatonia, however, is a tendency for such patients to fall into a stuporose condition. This may endure for a considerable period during which the person appears quite unaware of the presence of others and will not respond to the remarks of parents or physicians. This condition represents the most extreme from of withdrawal from life, short of suicide.

Paranoid schizophrenia is by far the most common form of this illness. The persecutionary delusions characteristic of such a disorder are not so highly organized as those of paranoia proper. These are always changing from one object to another, and are loosely held together. Thus the patient tends to look on everyone in his immediate environment as more or less his enemies intent on harming him. When he becomes a hospital patient the delusions usually fasten on members of the medical or nursing staff: he will complain of ill-treatment by some of these. He may suspect, for example, attempts on their part to poison him, and so may refuse medication and be generally uncooperative, hostile, and aggressive. Many of these patients behave almost as irrationally as a true paranoiac. They make frequent visits to their lawyer, and always with fresh 'evidence' of the hostility of their alleged enemies. Should the practitioner thus consulted not appear to be fighting their battles with sufficient vigour and success, or should he question the reality of their complaints, then they will turn to some other member of the legal profession. Not having much, or any, insight, they can see no reason why they are retained, or 'incarcerated' as they say, in hospital. Hospitalization, however, is essential in their own interests as well as in those of the public.

As a rule in these patients grandiose delusions will be found side by side with those of a persecutory nature. On this account it may be difficult at first to distinguish between this illness and that of mania—the symptoms of which will be described in a subsequent section. However, the complete picture of the one is quite different from that of the other; and the delusions of grandeur only serve greatly to strengthen those of persecution, the deluded individuals regarding themselves as people of unusual dignity and importance. Hence they are liable to become ferociously angry and aggressive against their alleged enemies. Sometimes however, they react in a different way— with utter disdain, indifference, and even pity for their 'miserable' persecutors.

Although it is helpful to be able to distinguish between these three types of schizophrenic illness, it must not be assumed that every patient of this kind fits neatly into one or other of the categories mentioned. As in the case of temperaments there is always some overlapping and mixing of schizophrenic symptoms. At the same time it is usually not difficult to discover which type of symptom predominates in the picture that a particular patient presents, and accordingly to make the diagnosis as specific as possible.

Sometimes what are undoubtedly obsessional symptoms are present in schizophrenia. This is particularly so during the early stages of the illness, especially in its hebephrenic form. The following excerpts from a letter written by a perplexed father about his son's behaviour, illustrate how such an illness may at first manifest itself. It will be noticed that already the withdrawal tendency is in evidence, also that the patient has changed from being a co-operative and normal person to one who cannot control his emotions, who gives way to violent temper tantrums and has become negative and aggressive. No hallucinations or delusions, however, of the typical kind have so far appeared; but insight is already showing signs of impairment. In part, the letter reads,

I have hesitated to write to you because I was hoping for an improvement in my son's ways, but I regret to say that there is no change. In many ways he is very intelligent but has a violent temper, is very selfish, argues a lot about the most simple things, is disobedient and persists in having his own way in all things. No matter what I do for him he does not show the slightest appreciation. Immediately one demand is met he wants something more, forgets past kindnesses, and concentrates on the immediate demand. . . . At eleven years of age he won a scholarship which qualified him to enter the local grammar school. At this time he appeared quite normal. After a time at the grammar school his reports became quite bad. The Headmaster told me that he was lazy, would not work at school and did no homework. I discovered later that instead of going to school he was going for walks through the country or sitting in the public library.

During his last term at school he was absent fifty-six days. He refused to take part in sports, pretending to be ill. Recently he has taken up a most peculiar attitude. He has told me that he will not have any interference from me, that he must be left alone to do his work as he pleases. . . . All this was shouted at me at the top of his voice in a most angry manner. He has violent arguments with his mother, sister and myself immediately anything is mentioned to him. He has a habit of repeating the same thing over and over again, for example, if he asked for anything, and there was not a prompt answer he would go on repeating the question, ignoring the fact that we were discussing something of importance, and shouting louder and louder. He suspects everything we say and finds fault with everything we do. He examines cups, saucers, and everything he uses, for dust. He talks a lot about T.B. infection from milk and washes his hands dozens of time daily. When he goes to bed he locks the bedroom door, and also spends long periods in the bathroom. When questioned about these things he gives the most ignorant and annoying answers. He is devoid of any sense of responsibility. He has broken watches, clocks, furniture by using them as 'playthings' and he never expresses regret for anything he destroys. A slide rule made of ivory which I prized, also a scaled rule and other instruments have all been used for various purposes, and smashed. He seems to think that everyone is trying to make little of him, or are laughing at him.

PARAPHRENIA

This psychosis and paranoid schizophrenia resemble each other so closely that it is difficult to draw a sharp distinction between them. Indeed, psychiatrists themselves seem to use the terms interchangeably—at least what some describe as symptoms of paranoid schizophrenia others refer to as those of paraphrenia. Drever's *Dictionary of Psychology* says that paraphrenia is a general term including both paranoia and schizophrenia, but most modern psychiatrists would put it differently by stating that paraphrenia is paranoid schizophrenia at an advanced level of that illness. Perhaps this is as near the truth as any statement can be; and, for practical purposes, it matters little which title we use. It needs, however, to be emphasized that paraphrenic patients are more highly deluded and hallucinated than paranoid schizophrenics, also that the hallucinations that affect them are usually of the auditory rather than of the visual kind. Moreover, whilst these patients are not free from some elements of grandiose delusions and states of exaltation, yet in the main the delusions are persecutory, and frequently take the form of warnings of impending crimes in which both themselves and their relatives will undergo appalling suffering. These messages reach them through wireless, radar, and telephone calls, as well as in and through veiled newspaper references. Some become convinced that they are the subjects of baneful influences which affect them in all manner of harmful ways. This may mean that electric currents are being directed against them, or that they are being controlled by suggestion. Many of them think that the injections they receive in hospital are deliberately intended to do them bodily harm; and the same is true of the medication they undergo. Some speak about 'the killing injections' they are receiving, and of the fact that the entire aim in their hospitalization is to bring about their death by slow means. The following lines from a paraphrenic's letter are typical.

> The interference with my body disturbs me. On my body is nothing visible, but the interferences are all there. Let me relate the last occurrences. Mr — was in the hospital one day last week. After being served with information regarding me he went away immediately. Two days later Dr — called and asked me several questions which I answered quietly and correctly. After this he went away. I cannot help to have the impression that he thought the tempo of my being killed has been too slow and unsatisfactory for him. The other members of the staff found a much cruder method which is applied at me. Yesterday the nurse distributed tablets. He gave me one resembling a salmon-pink lozenger against which I protested, but afterwards my inner parts started to burn from the throat all the way down to the stomach. I took some milk and one aspirin. The burning ceased after about one hour. Next night the same kind of lozenger was forced down my throat. It had the same bad taste, but the quantum must have been far greater. I took two cups of milk and one aspirin. I fell asleep and wakened at about 4 with pains in my legs. I was rushed down the corridor. Subsequently my breath became shorter and faster. Yesterday injections were directed in a way that affected my *aorta*. These gave me severe cramps, my legs and neck being affected. The action was directed against my arteries. I am wondering how long these attacks and machinations are to go on, but there must come a time soon when the final reaction will end my sufferings.

A letter, descriptive of early paraphrenic symptoms, received from an anxious brother contained the following lines:

> He hates to have to go out, because he thinks everyone is looking at him, and talking about him. He also thinks that his clothes

are marked in such a way that people everywhere he goes make derogatory comments about them. He thinks that all his money is counterfeit and that he will get into trouble for using it. Even the money he draws direct from the bank he thinks is specially given him so that he will get into trouble.

Two considerations suggest that these ideas (usually called 'ideas of reference') are paraphrenic. In the first place the man maintained perfect mental health until he was fifty-eight years of age. If they were paranoid schizophrenic symptoms they would most likely have begun much earlier. Secondly, at a later stage, the typical paraphrenic delusions and auditory hallucinations developed, and the persecutory factor took on the gravest turn; for he became convinced that for the 'crimes' he had committed he would have to suffer the extreme penalty of death by hanging.

The prognosis in cases of paraphrenia is most unfavourable. Yet experience has taught me never to dogmatize too freely regarding this. For example, one person who was for some time amongst the most agitated and deluded of mental patients, and for whose recovery doctors had but slender hope, quite suddenly became like her real self. All her delusions cleared up; and for the last two years she has been able to carry out her regular duties with no sign of any reaction. This person believed that people were plotting against herself and her relatives. All were to be destroyed, and on a particular day, by a gang which was even now fully ready for the fatal attack. The women of the family were first to be abducted and raped, after which all were to be strangled. This disaster, she said, was the result of 'something her forebears had done in the seventeenth century'. This had so displeased the Almighty, she said, that 'He is now about to take vengeance on their children and children's children unto the third and fourth generation.' Here surely is evidence of that complete lack of insight which we associate with gross mental disorder.

I was interested to know what explanation this patient would give when the day on which the supposed disaster was to happen had passed without incident. So I visited her home that evening only to find that she had an answer ready. It was to the effect that God had sent her a message through radio that the disaster had been postponed for a week; but no explanation of the delay was added.

PSYCHOPATHY

This term is used by psychiatrists with even less consistency than paraphrenia. Some doctors use it without further distinction, for all types of psychotic illness. Apart from schizophrenia, the Greek derivations of these names do not throw much light on the actual difference, if any, between them. Thus paraphrenia comes from *para* and *phren* which should mean 'beside oneself', while psychopathy comes from *psyche* and *pascho* meaning 'mental suffering'.

However, it is desirable to fix the definite characteristics of these psychoses, so far as this is at all possible. We have tried to do so in regard to paraphrenia. What is there to be said regarding the distinctive features of psychopathy?

It would be generally agreed that this is mainly a *behaviour-disorder*. Psychotics are people who are seriously unaware in any real sense of the difference between right and wrong. Some of them may have a particularly high intelligence quotient, like a true paranoiac, yet be completely devoid of any moral sense. They may *know* that they commit crimes, and that these are liable to lead to punishment; but they manifest no signs of any *feeling* of having done wrong; nor do they ever repent, or learn lessons from their punishments. They, like schizophrenics, will manifest instability of personality and lack of persistence. Hence they do not remain at school or college for any length of time; nor will they remain at work in any business except for brief periods. So they tend to drift from one failure to another until they deteriorate into drug addicts, alcoholics, sexual perverts, or become spongers or ne'er-do-wells in society. The one thing about them that is significant is the way in which they set their minds on *near goals*, by means of which some satisfactions may be achieved, regardless of ultimate consequences. Hence, as we have said, they learn no lessons from experience; and so there is every likelihood that their anti-social behaviour will continue unmodified to the end of their days. One person who behaved like a typical psychopath belonged to a most highly-respected and intelligent family. From the time of his adolescence he gave his parents trouble by refusing to remain at school or in business for any appreciable period. What was even more distressing for them was his habit of petty pilfering—at first in the home and then from others in school and business. Later on more serious crimes were planned; for a psychopath may be venturesome without having any conscience. This person managed to get his hands on his mother's cheque-book. He forged cheques for considerable amounts and then absconded to England where he lived in various hotels until all the money had been spent. Then, like the Prodigal, when he had spent all, he came home. Unlike the Prodigal, however, there were no signs of regret or of penitence; nor was any apology made for the distress and shame which his behaviour had caused his parents. He knew he had done wrong; but he had learned no lessons from his mistakes; nor had he ever experienced any sense of guilt for his delinquencies. The typical answer of a psychopath to any leading question about his conduct is, 'What I do is my own business, and I wish people would leave me alone.'

Dr Stafford-Cark says that there are two things to be remembered about psychopaths. The first is, as just stated, that there is little hope of their behaviour ever undergoing any material change. The second is that the psychopathic personality appears to rest on certain physical and emotional factors, the former of which still remain vague while the latter is best described as immaturity in its most comprehensive sense (*Psychiatry To-day*, 117).

Many of those who have to be retained in 'special care' hospitals, or in training schools, are psychopathic in their make-up. One wonders if there is any hope of permanent improvement through the disciplinary training which these institutions necessarily provide, or if religion can do anything to create a genuine conscience in those who seem to be completely devoid of any moral sense.

PARANOID TRENDS

One of the lessons learnt through experience in dealing with mental illnesses is that even the psychiatrist cannot be too cautious in coming to conclusions regarding the interpretation of particular symptoms. This has been well illustrated by Professor Harold de Wolf of Boston University, in a story about a woman supposed to be the victim of paranoid delusions, who had been sent to a mental hospital. He was amongst several ministers of religion and others, who had been invited to a psychiatric clinic to receive instruction on the typical symptoms of various forms of mental illness. One of those presented was the particular person whose case he describes. The doctors drew out her story of persistent persecutions, and of conspiracies against her by her own relatives. She explained that she had a case against a Steamship Company which she was confident of winning. The only point now in doubt was the precise amount of damages which she would receive, but she was sure to receive a fabulous sum—so large that her family had decided to 'railroad' her to a mental institution in a bid to get their hands on her estate. In great detail she went through her story, and when she had come to the end of it she was escorted back to her room, where, as an alleged dangerous paranoiac, she had been kept away from other patients.

Later on the doctor in charge decided, out of sheer interest, to investigate more thoroughly than had already been done the woman's background, with a view to discovering whether there was any real basis for the elaborate and fantastic story. As a result of this, the same group was urgently invited back to the hospital to be informed that the doctors had been guilty of a grave misdiagnosis in her case, and that everything about which she had complained was true down to the last detail. Here was a person relating experiences which had actually taken place, although during the recital doctors and ministers had stood round with notebooks and pencils feverishly jotting down what they regarded as the pathological ravings of a disordered mind.

The story is told in *The Theology of a Living Church* (p. 59), and the moral is that no minister, or psychiatrist, should ever jump to rash conclusions regarding the precise interpretations of symptoms, no matter how typical of certain psychoses these may appear to be. On the other hand we have to beware of making another type of mistake, namely that of regarding false rumours of a scandalous nature circulated by an actual paranoiac who is believed by his hearers to be a normal person. In nine cases out of ten, for instance, where stories of a husband's unfaithfulness and neglect are broadcast without restraint, then one can almost assume that the wife who makes the complaints is probably a victim of paranoic delusions.

The possibility, moreover, has to be kept in mind that symptoms, indistinguishable from paranoid or paraphrenic delusions, may, as a matter of fact, be rather the secondary, paranoid effects of an acute guilt complex. Thus many years ago the husband of a woman who believed that the 'spiritualists' were experimenting on her brain asked me to see her and give him advice regarding her treatment. During the first interview the woman went into great detail in describing the activities of these mysterious enemies, who, she alleged, visited her only at night, and made sure that she was fast asleep before they began their 'experimentations'. Other typical persecutory delusions were also so much in evidence that I had no hesitation in conveying to her husband a very gloomy picture of her condition, and in advising him to call in his doctor and seek psychiatric treatment for her. Meanwhile I continued to call as frequently as possible simply to allow her to unburden her mind, and at the same time to give her such assurance as she could appreciate.

One day, however, when I called as usual, to my surprise I found her in a much less agitated mood than I had expected. She began to talk more rationally, and finally said she wished to 'make a confession'. She was encouraged to do so. Then there came from her lips a long and pathetic story of the loneliness which she had experienced in the early years of her married life. Her husband had frequently had to be away on professional business; and when he was at home these duties seemed to occupy every moment of his time, so that she felt neglected, frustrated, and resentful. Then a neighbour, not of her sex, began to visit her during her husband's absence, with what results we leave it to the reader to imagine. The fact, however, was that the subsequent years witnessed a gradual deterioration in her relationships with her husband. Her irritability towards him, coupled with hatred of herself, revealed the extent to which she had been the victim of an uneasy conscience. In due time she repressed the guilt associated with the incident; then, as usually happens, she projected it first on others—for she had become a carping critic of a most objectionable type—and, later, through the mechanism of projection, developed the delusion from which she was suffering. These 'spiritualists', she averred, were earnestly intent on discovering the hidden guilty secrets of her past life. The complete and sudden change of mood that had taken place, together with the disappearance of the delusion, and also the fact that no hereditary factor could be traced in her family history, combined to make it abundantly clear that, although the symptoms were those we associate with a paranoid condition, they were, as we have suggested, rather the secondary, paranoid effects of a severe guilt complex.

Once again the same moral is implied in this as in the former story—that all rash conclusions in our efforts to understand those who appear to be victims of psychotic symptoms must be avoided, and that, in any case, ministers themselves should never attempt to label a particular type of illness, no matter how definite the symptoms may be. This should be left to the psychiatrist, the reasons being that not only may an amateur diagnosis be quite erroneous, but also 'unqualified' people run grave legal risks in giving expression to their ideas on the subject.

At the beginning of this chapter, reference was made to the prevalence of paranoid 'trends' in the character and behaviour of many who are generally accepted as normal members of society. This often seems to run in families; but it is more likely, although in less serious ways than in the story just related, to give point to the contention already made, just how seriously an unrelieved guilt-problem may affect the spirit and character of many people. These are often prominent members in the church, and are the types likely to suffer from slight delusions of reference, that is to say taking to themselves, personally, comments made by the minister of others which are not intended to apply to them; complaining, for example, that they are passed over when appointments are made to official positions in the church, or that their characters are being discussed when they are not present. Frequently these unite with others of similar mood and disposition, and may become so disgruntled that they decide to leave their church and either join one of the neurotic sects described in an earlier chapter, or inaugurate a little sect of their own.

It is not, of course, to be assumed that those who make complaints regarding the policy of the church to which they belong, or who criticize the behaviour of some of its officials, are always to be understood as 'personalizing their own unrecognized failings'—to use Dr Hadfield's expression. Just and constructive criticisms, made in the spirit of love and concern for the well-being of the church, or of some church member, are often a duty from which responsible Christians should not shrink; but in making them, one must never forget that no one is quite normal; nor is anyone completely free from fault. The case-book of a psychiatrist—one of the most entertaining works I have ever read—has the suggestive title *A Few Buttons Missing*. The author, who was brought up on an American farm, tells the story of a cow—we shall call her Nellie—which he describes as a 'rugged individualist'. 'Even before we got out of the lane in the morning she'd plant herself wrong way of the herd, and commence nudging the flanks of the other cattle filing past. Just plain ornery. At the creek she'd wade out to midstream and drink; and then stand there with water dripping from her mouth while she surveyed the landscape in all directions, like a quarterback looking over the field before calling the next play.' Old Nellie remained a cow, but how different from other cows! So it is with human beings; not only lots of youthful delinquents and elderly 'cranks', but large numbers of those who constitute the human 'herd' are a bit like a human version of old Nellie. They spend most of their years in breaking away from the human group, and making life miserable for all who try to keep them 'on the clearly defined trail of social acceptability.' But then we are all a little 'queer', and it is well to remember this, for it helps to check the human tendency (which is a sign of our Original Sin) to degenerate into chronic fault-finders, and, what is even more prevalent, to be suspicious of the motives from which others act, when they profess to do so for the most charitable ends.

Finally, so far as paranoid *trends* are concerned, we find that to be able to master this tendency it is sufficient for people to become aware of its presence—and to be able to master it is utterly impossible unless to this extent self-knowledge has been gained. As Dr Colton, a well-known American psychiatrist, puts it, 'It is with diseases of the mind as with those of the body, we are half dead before we understand our disorder, and half cured when we do.'

DEPRESSIVE STATES

Depression is one of the most distressing of all human experiences, and is one from which no human being escapes. Two main types of this disorder can be easily distinguished—simple or rational depression, and depression described in textbooks as pathological or endogenous. We have to indicate the differences between these if we are to give the proper guidance to those concerned either directly or indirectly with it.

The former type—a universal experience—arises from difficulties, frustrations, disappointments, failures, and a host of similar unpalatable events of daily occurrence, of which the person affected is well aware. The speed with which his mood of depression can be overcome depends on such factors as the seriousness of the event itself and on the temperamental quality of the sufferer and the courage with which he faces his problem. Quick *action* to deal with any situation which causes simple depression is an important habit to establish, whilst any tendency to brood over one's failures is fatal since this only serves to make those with whom we live as miserable as ourselves. It also deepens our own feelings of gloom. Bereavement, in certain circumstances—as when the person taken is young or is almost indispensable to us—is a much deeper and more persistent type of depression. This experience receives fuller attention in a subsequent chapter, so here we shall be content merely to state that (unless a morbid factor is involved) time will always prove itself to be, to at least a considerable extent, a rectifier and healer.

Endogenous depression is much more serious than the simple, reactive type to which we have so far alluded. It is also much more difficult to treat. Thus to urge patients who are downcast because of unforeseen reverses and disappointments to 'pull themselves together' may be good advice, but to offer the same advice to those afflicted with pathological depression will prove worse than useless, and may do positive harm. One may as well urge someone suffering from a serious organic illness to conquer their symptoms by will power, as to expect morbidly depressed persons to do so by similar effort. The reason is, of course, that we are now concerned with an illness the cause of which is obscure and altogether unknown to the patient himself, although he may relate it to some external happening, or indeed, when insight has become impaired, to some ridiculously trivial or imaginary 'sin'. Thus one patient attributed her utterly hopeless condition to the fact that she had induced her husband to sell the ancestral home and purchase a more modern one. Shortly after this transaction her illness began, so it was natural for her to infer that she was being punished by God for the 'grave sin' for which she made herself responsible. She began to persuade her husband to seek to regain possession of her former dwelling. He did so with the result that her illness became all the more acute.

MANIC-DEPRESSIVE PSYCHOSIS

There are two types of endogenous depression which every minister should be able to distinguish. One of these is known as manic-depressive psychosis and the other melancholia.

The former is characterized, as the name indicates, by an alternation of mood from one of abnormal elation to one of utter despair. Whatever be the main cause of the illness, the swing from one extreme of mood to its opposite is usually attributed to what is called a 'cyclothymic' type of temperament.

In the elated phase the patient manifests unusual activity both of body and of mind. He becomes abnormally loquacious and will jump from one idea to another with little or no connexion between the two. He will take to writing long, rambling letters to distinguished people in which religious thoughts, quotations from the Bible and hymn-books, and obscene remarks are all jumbled together. He develops grandiose delusions regarding himself and his achievements and may write to government departments announcing some wonderful invention which could be used for the purpose of the particular department with magic effect. He may pose as some world-renowned figure, such as the late Sir Winson Churchill, and sit all day in perfect self-composure smoking a cigar.

Unless the patient is a case of chronic mania he will, sooner or later, lapse into a condition of dejection and present the extreme opposite picture of his former self. Thus he will become dull and lethargic and will move about—if he moves at all—with slowness of pace and with head down and shoulders drooped. He will withdraw from social life, and is likely to develop delusions precisely the opposite of those characteristic of manic patients. The latter may imagine themselves million-aires and write their minister a cheque for thousands of pounds 'for his work' and add a cheque for a considerable sum for his own 'personal use'. The pathologically depressed person, on the other hand, may develop a delusion of abject poverty.

On one occasion I was privileged to accompany some friends on a journey to the summit of Snowdon. We were hoping to experience what others had described as 'one of the thrills of their life', provided in the panoramic view from the top. However, on this occasion we found ourselves, on reaching the end of the journey, enshrouded in deep, dark cloud and mist which completely wiped out the view. About to entrain for the downward journey, a very much disappointed party, the unbelievable happened; back rolled the blanket of cloud and out came the sun in all his splendour, presenting us with one of the most wonderful views I had ever witnessed, although on more than one occasion I had experienced the awesomeness of the Rocky Mountains of Canada.

It is always like this with manic-depressive patients. They may be assured that in time—sometimes more quickly than at other times, and for no apparent reason—the clouds round about their spirits will lift, and for them life will become, for the time being at least, even more exhilarating than it is for most of those who never fall into the 'valley of despair'. On the calendar of the day, a patient once read some lines from the writings of St Thomas à Kempis: 'It will pass; it has happened before; if you live long enough it will happen again.' The words 'it will pass' resulted in the emergence of an immediate ray of hope, and, after that, the expression became to this patient a 'gospel' which, he said, met his need more effectively than even the doctor's prescriptions.[1]

Psychiatrists on the whole would agree that manic-depressive illness is the most benign of all the psychoses, and that a large proportion of those affected in this way will recover. They also admit that psychological talks can assist in some of the milder forms of this illness—especially where a considerable measure of insight has been maintained by the patient.

MELANCHOLIA

The main difference between melancholia and the depressed phase of the psychosis we have been describing is that the former is a chronic condition in the sense that it does not alternate with elation. It can occur in two forms, one a condition of deep gloom and retardation, and the other a condition in which despair is accompanied with much agitation.

The first may be illustrated from a situation commonly witnessed in a factory where night workers are busy, where powerful electric lights have the effect of turning night into day, where one can hear the constant thud of engines and other machinery, and where a continuous output of valuable products for export is taking place. This suggests the situation where a person is buoyantly healthy in body and mind. However, it is possible that owing to some serious fault in an electric main the entire situation may suddenly alter. No one at first, and prior to investigation by the expert, can dogmatically say what has happened. But the lights have gone out in a moment, the machinery has suddenly stopped, the output of products has ceased and all activity on the part of the workers has ended.

How similar the picture of the typical melancholic! Normally interested in life and business and home, he now manifests and feels no interest in anything. His condition is characterized by withdrawal from social life; devoid of his usual energy he is no longer an active participant in the affairs of business, or home, or church life. He becomes apathetic in the extreme so that good news and bad are both alike to him. His retardation is a

[1] This illness is also treated in my book *Disorders of the Emotional and Spiritual Life*, Chapter 1.

surprise to all who knew him in his normal health. The remark, 'he is the last person I would have expected to become like this' is often heard amongst his associates and friends, and, being a church worker as so many melancholics have been, the question will naturally be asked, 'Why has he not been helped by his religious faith?' To which one answer, of course, would be, 'Why do Christians suffer as others do from diseases of the body?' In this connexion also it might be well to remind the afflicted and anxious person that many of the great saints and classical mystics had their times of the deepest spiritual despair. These they described as 'the dark night of the soul'.

The picture of melancholia which psychiatry draws for us, and of which all ministers are bound to have some knowledge from their pastoral experience, is in broad outline, as already indicated, no different from the depressed phase of the manic-depressive patient. However, as we have also explained, this condition is chronic in the sense that it does not alternate with a phase of elation, and although spontaneous recovery often happens and the use of drugs or electric convulsive treatment can help, the prognosis is not so favourable as that of manic-depressives', chiefly, perhaps, because this clouding of the spirit takes place most frequently in the latter decades of life, and may be, in part, attributable to the fact that the time of retirement is coming appreciably nearer.

To the other form of melancholia proper is given the name of involutional melancholia, apparently because of its relation to the climacteric. It is more serious and the picture it presents is more pathetic than either of the other forms of depression to which reference has been made. Patients suffering in this way are acutely agitated. They live wholly in the past and spend much of their time searching through their experience for memories of incidents by which they condemn themselves. Often the most trifling errors are exaggerated by them into enormities. They become the subjects of pathological guilt (to which we shall make reference later) and are liable to develop in a serious way the 'unpardonable sin' delusion. This, we have seen, can emerge in some forms of obsessional neurosis, but it is possible in the ways indicated, to relieve the distress thus caused in the case of a neurosis. It is otherwise in psychotic illness, where the patient has completely lost insight and is incapable either of exercising personal faith or co-operating with his medical or spiritual advisers.

Since this is the type of patient who is likely, without warning, to take his life, institutional treatment is absolutely necessary and the minister should urge relatives to seek medical and psychiatric help towards this end, again insisting that in these enlightened days, there is no stigma to be attached to this procedure. Moreover, institutional treatment provides the sedation they need, since these patients suffer much from insomnia, and in addition it sets relatives free from the intolerable strain of attempting to care for them.

TREATMENT OF PSYCHOTIC ILLNESS

The prognosis in cases of psychotic illness is very uncertain, but with the use of more up-to-date medication—which to some extent has taken the place of electric convulsive treatment—the outlook for large numbers of such patients is now by no means so gloomy as it once was. We shall be referring at length to this hopeful situation in the chapter on 'Drugs and Religion'. There has been a more controversial method of treatment which is used as a last resort in instances in which all other types of treatment has failed. This is generally known by the name 'leucotomy', or, more recently, psychosurgery. It is an operation in which certain nerve fibres connecting the frontal lobes with the rest of the brain are severed. Patients have to be very carefully selected for this operation, which was once cruder and more complicated than it is at present. It was objected to strongly by the relatives of patients who understood that, while it may eliminate dominant symptoms, it may also have the effect of reducing the personality to a mere 'cabbage'. However, as at present undertaken there is little danger of any such extreme effects, and some of those on whom this operation has been carried out now live a fairly normal life. There is one danger, however, connected with psychosurgery, namely the possibility of so reducing thereby the person's powers of self-control that he may find himself unable to resist outbursts of passionate hatred against relatives and, indeed, become homicidal. For this reason a growing number of psychiatrists are refusing to recommend such drastic treatment in any circumstances. Meantime ministers should, on every possible occasion, praise the work of psychiatrists, nurses, and mental health associations for the marvellous and growing success that is attending their efforts to cure the mentally ill, short of the expedient of psychosurgery.

SEVEN

Insomnia and Suicide

The minister's pastoral responsibilities will bring him into contact with those who will complain, amongst other things, of inability to sleep. Less frequently he will find himself called upon to minister to the families of those who have taken their own lives. In such circumstances he will require all the resources both of psychological knowledge and of religion to ensure that his pastoral visit will have a comforting and healing effect.

That there is a close connexion between insomnia and suicide should be obvious to those who have had any experience of ministering to involutional melancholics. We remember that these patients suffer much from insomnia; also that they are the type most likely to commit suicide. In fact, however, the possibility of giving way to self-destructive impulses must not be ruled out wherever there is deep depression of any kind coupled with insomnia.

SLEEPLESSNESS AND INSOMNIA

In dealing first with the problem of insomnia, it may be worthwhile to indicate the difference between sleeplessness and insomnia proper. The former is to be thought of as merely a temporary phase due to some special difficulties, whether business, family, or personal, which the individual concerned is finding it difficult to solve. A family quarrel, for example, can disturb one's sleep for many nights until the situation eases, and reconciliation is effected. Where difficult business problems arise, sleeplessness may continue for some time. In such circumstances it is not easy to dissociate one's mind from one's affairs; but unless this is done, deep and continuous sleep becomes next to impossible. Some insomniacs manage to fall asleep almost at once; but then, within an hour or two, they will become wide awake and remain so for the rest of the night. Others simply cannot sleep at all until it is almost time to face the duties of a new day. This, if it continues, can have serious results on one's nervous and physical health. It means facing the responsibilities and irritations of the day, but with judgement, temper, and resolution—all very necessary for successful work—appreciably diminished. There is no very satisfactory explanation available regarding the nature of sleep, and why people require to spend a third of their time abed. It is obvious, of course, that sleep has marvellous recuperative and healing powers; but then experience shows how refreshed one can become even after a twenty-minute nap. Why then should it take seven or eight hours to do what, apparently, can be done in twenty minutes? It is said, too, by way of explanation, that life is on a rhythmic basis of waking and sleeping, consciousness and unconsciousness, activity and rest, and that these movements alternate with day and night. Again, however, this is not a universal experience. Some animals sleep all day and hunt for their prey all night; others hibernate throughout the winter. Once more: human beings can accustom themselves, as, for example, doctors and nurses must, to sleep during daylight and work through the hours of darkness.

Dr Crichton-Miller, to whose book *Insomnia* we have already referred, summarized in the opening pages all the known theories of sleep, but was forced to confess at the end that the only conclusion to which he could come was that sleep was 'instinctive', and leave the matter there. The remainder of the book, then, was devoted to conditions of sleep and to a consideration of factors which prevented it from taking place.

We must keep in mind the fact alluded to in the chapter on 'The Problem of "Nerves"' that human beings suffer more from strain than lower animals do, and this because of the unique qualities of mind and heart in the former, which the latter do not have. This applies also to the problem of sleeplessness, which, of course, is closely related to 'nerves'. The animal lies down and goes readily to sleep as though without a care in the world. Many members of the human family have the same gift, which the less favoured greatly envy. The animals require no training in special techniques to induce sleep. A large proportion of human beings do require some artificial aids and the practice of certain techniques before conditions conducive to sleep can be established.

We have found it a useful aid for those afflicted in this way to talk quietly with them over some techniques found to be helpful. Thus we are familiar with the suggestion, often made, that sleepless individuals might spend some time 'counting sheep as they jump over stiles'. We have never had many testimonies to the effectiveness of this device, but the idea implied in it is important, namely, that sleep is possible only when the mind becomes detached from its worries. It is when the mind is over-active that people cannot sleep. So, as one retires to rest it is important to be able to dissociate oneself from the irritations of the day.

Secondly, it is helpful to remind those who cannot sleep that all their worries appear to be grossly exaggerated and completely out of focus, between midnight and the early hours of morning. This should be the starting point for a general conversation on the importance or relative unimportance of the things about which people become distressed, and how when, as Bishop Butler used to say, 'we sit down in a cool hour' and give attention to these we shall be able to see them in a new and less distorted perspective. There is a passage in Job worth recalling in this connexion: 'In thought, in visions of the night, when deep sleep falleth upon me, fear came on me and trembling which made all my bones to shake. Then a spirit passed before my face, the hair of my head stood up.' For Job things were out of focus at midnight, as they are for so many in these modern days, so let us remind those afflicted by sleeplessness that the same situations which make sleep intermittent, and even disturbing, always appear less ominous in the day time.

Thirdly, conversation with one who finds sleep difficult to achieve should deal with the danger of substituting sleeplessness itself for the initial causes of our sleeplessness. Thus at first sleep becomes intermittent or impossible because of some domestic or business problem. Later the harmful effects of wakefulness become the greater cause of our inability to 'lay ourselves down in peace to sleep'.

Fourthly, ministers should be alive to the danger that people who for a time and for simple reasons only manage to get snatches of sleep, may imagine that a temporary phase of sleeplessness is an early symptom of a serious mental illness, which will inevitably end in confinement in a psychiatric hospital. Any such fear should be resolutely rejected by the person's spiritual adviser, and his mind should be made easy regarding any such eventuality.

Fifthly, psychological magazines often carry recipes which are supposed to work wonders for those who cannot conquer, by any effort of will, this particular disability. One of these makes much of the idea already referred to as important, namely, as complete a state of physical relaxation as possible. Here is how one magazine article puts it: 'Think first of the muscles of your scalp, the top of your head. Relax these muscles. Now concentrate on the muscles of your forehead. Feel the muscles sag. Now your eyelids. Relax them. They are so heavy you can't lift them. Now the muscles of your face. Let the muscles go. Your jaws—let them sag. Note especially your neck. Move your head around until your neck is so relaxed that your head feels a dead weight. Drop it—let it roll until it comes to a stop by itself. Go right down your back. Feel the muscles let go. Let your mind follow down each arm, relaxing the shoulders, the elbows, the wrists, each finger. Now consider the muscles of your chest. Relax them. Then your stomach. Let everything sag. Heavy. Heavy. Feel the heaviness of your hips pushing against the bed. Now relax each, thigh, foot, toe. Slowly. Slowly . . . you're asleep.'

'All very well,' says the reader, 'but it is not so easy to make the technique work.' Most people who attempt it find it impossible to switch the mind, with its worries, to the body in the way advised. They can do so momentarily, but back will turn the mind again and again to its problems. It must be admitted, however, that relaxation is a condition of refreshing and prolonged sleep, and this, rather than any effort of will, or struggle to conquer sleeplessness is the way by which people so afflicted can help themselves. Physical relaxation, indeed, in the way prescribed, is a form of self-hypnosis which—in what we call here sleeplessness in contrast to insomnia—may, by persistent trying, become an established habit. In this con-nexion it should always be remembered that if, as Dr Crichton-Miller suggests, sleep is instinctive, then we need not struggle for it. If we relax and allow it to fall upon us it should do so, and if we are not always achieving the normal seven or eight hours of uninterrupted sleep but can make up for shorter periods at night by the 'after-dinner nap', then there is no need whatsoever to be concerned over this matter. At any rate it is believed that some can do with much less sleep than others, and, of course, elderly folk never sleep anything like the 'round of the clock'. They have no need to.

Ministers, themselves, one should add, suffer as much as most others through sleeplessness. This is natural, of course, for example, on Sunday nights, when we find ourselves inclined to repeat our sermons after reaching home, either to ourselves or to an imaginary congregation. Most ministers realize, as they engage in this bad practice, how preoccupied the mind becomes regarding the blemishes in the sermon itself and the defects of the method of delivery. They dwell on the ways in which the entire plan and content of the sermon could have been improved. They know, however, that sleeplessness produced by such thoughts is not serious, and that they will usually sleep without difficulty every other night of the week. At the same time this habit may cause considerable worry to those who foolishly stake their reputation on what happens in the pulpit. One minister known to me acknowledged how much he fretted if the number present in the congregation at a particular service was not up to standard. He wondered if his people were getting tired of his preaching. This man had to withdraw from the active ministry at a very early age because of ill-health. Had he adopted a more relaxed attitude to all his work, his ministry would have been more effective and pro-longed, and his health would not have become so quickly impaired. Basically, worry over such matters is indicative of a sensitiveness regarding one's reputation which is actually a subtle form of pride.

Insomnia proper is much more deeply rooted and serious than simple sleeplessness. It is not a mere habit, but is a symptom of illness. Already we have seen that it is a major symptom of involutional melancholia. Patients afflicted in this way can be treated only by the strongest drugs or by electric convulsive therapy. They certainly cannot respond either to psychological or spiritual therapy. Informed pastoral practice, on the other hand, can be helpful when one is dealing with an insomniac capable of understanding and responding to advice and suggestion. Dr Crichton-Miller's book *Insomnia*, already referred to, is devoted mainly to cases of hysteria in which insomnia always serves a useful purpose; although the patient himself is usually unaware of this fact. The following case-history explains how insomnia may arise in a hysterical patient, and the kind of purpose which it may serve.

A young man with unusual gifts of personality and facility for effective public speaking experienced a catastrophic and intensely emotional conversion at evangelistic services in which the influence of mass suggestion was almost irresistible. Immediately afterwards he was persuaded to 'give his testimony' at the annual convention organized by the particular denomination which had shown a keen interest in him and had succeeded in inducing him to leave his own Church. So 'electric' was the impression he made that then and there he was chosen as the chief speaker at the annual convention of the sect. This was only the first of a series of such engagements. In course of time, however, he began to realize that he had almost completely lost the 'spiritual glow' with which his religious pilgrimage had commenced. The more he struggled to have this experience restored the more it seemed to disappear, and was followed by what mystics call 'the dry period of the soul'. His main purpose, therefore, from that time forward, in attending and even in speaking at religious gatherings,was the salvation of his own soul. To this end also he became increasingly ascetic in his religious practices, refraining 'from all appearance of evil', and observing a rigid programme of fasting and other forms of self-denial. This he found to be unavailing; so, going even further, he made weekly visits to the top of a mountain not far from his home, where, after the manner of Christ, he 'continued all night in prayer to God'. This also failed to bring him the assurance he needed. Finally, on a particular Saturday night, while engaged in the preparation of a 'message' to be delivered next day at an important convention gathering, he experienced, quite suddenly, a most distressing 'migraine headache'. This was followed by a night of sleeplessness and mental distress. His doctor administered strong sedatives; but these had little effect on his condition; so he became the victim of one of the most acute forms of insomnia I have ever known. In their effort to help him back to health and happiness his medical advisers took the extreme step of recommending him to withdraw from business for a time. This he did, and retired to a remote part of the country in the hope that absoute quiet might do for him what medication had failed to effect. Such efforts, however, proved unavailing, as did the cruises on which he spent considerable sums of money. Eventually, in the light of psychological talks he saw clearly enough the purpose of his illness, which obviously was to extricate himself from a predicament with which he had not the courage to deal in a more direct and healthy manner. Contrary, however, to psychoanalytic teaching, this degree of enlightenment appeared to have little effect; for the particular symptom continued to trouble him. He had therefore to realize further that the symptom which had served to solve his original problem might still be needed to prevent any possible recurrence of it, through being induced to resume his convention activities. It was not, however, until he had seen that along with psychological enlightenment he needed a new understanding of the nature of Christian experience, and of the conditions of Christian discipleship, that release began to take place.

It must not be overlooked, of course, that insomnia proper may be rooted, not in any psychological disturbance or need, but in a morbid physical conditions, a fact which underlines the advice, already given so often in previous pages, that the direct treatment of any such illness is a matter for the doctor rather than for the pastor. The ability to understand such problems, however, is a most important qualification for effective pastoral practice.

SUICIDE

Not so long ago attempted suicide was regarded as an offence punishable by a period of imprisoument. It is difficult to think of any law more unjust or unwise; for if the first attempt has failed, the potential suicide is bound to try to take his life again merely to get rid of the stigma attached to the 'crime'.

At an early stage of my ministry I had this problem brought to my notice when a member of my congregation, reputed to be amongst the most happy of individuals, without any warning whatsoever attempted to commit suicide, and was brought for treatment to a hospital. When I went there, somewhat bewildered, I found to my further dismay a policeman posted at his bedside. This brought home to me the fact that, in the eyes of the law, the suicidal person is a criminal. Thus while in hospital he must be kept under strict supervision, and when discharged brought to trial and imprisoned. This man escaped such humiliation by surreptitiously taking into the bathroom an instrument with which in a few minutes he ended his life. Had there been at the time a different attitude towards suicide, and a more Christian way of dealing with the person who attempts it, this man could have been saved. It is strange that the Church, which insists on the sacredness of human life, should have tolerated so long such a short-sighted way of dealing with those who are obviously sick souls, who have injured no one but themselves, and, indeed, for whose plight society itself must share part of the blame.

Why do some people commit suicide? Not all who do so appear to be in any greater trouble than others. Statistics prove that the incidence of suicide does not depend solely on material conditions. In Sweden, for example, where the material standards of life are high, the number of suicides per thousand of the population is far greater than in less favoured countries. It may have some bearing on the problem, however, to know that there are more acts of self-destruction in city centres, where there are large concentrations of people, than in rural areas.

The most frequent answer, however, given to the question just posed, is that people commit suicide because they are in a state of 'unsound mind'. Already we have referred to the fact that suicide among involutional melancholics is always likely, or at least possible. These take their lives so as to escape from their imaginary 'executioners'. The paranoid schizophrenic may do so for very much the same reason. He, too, as we have seen, feels himself to be the victim of numerous 'enemies' all intent on doing him physical or mental harm. Some schizophrenics, moreover, may take their lives in obedience to what they interpret to be the command of God, which they say they distinctly hear. The voice so heard, of course, is a typical schizophrenic hallucinatory experience.

Not all, however, who commit suicide, are necessarily of unsound mind. They need not be even 'temporarily insane',

H

notwithstanding the fact that this explanation of their deed is the one most frequently given at inquests. It is believed that some possess what is described as a 'suicidal disposition', which is the basis of 'accident proneness'. Not all accidents in which people lose their lives are genuine accidents at all. For many have been influenced, or even determined, by 'unconscious suicidal motives'. Thus it is of intent, albeit unconscious, that so many fail to notice danger signals at street crossings, or along the seashore at places known to be treacherous. This is part of the meaning of what Freud called 'the psychopathology of everyday life'.

Less speculative is the view that some suicides are due to the turning of murderous hatred, against another, back on oneself. The Freudians speak of a death- as well as of a life-instinct, of which we all are subjects. The life instinct, however, is the stronger, mainly because self-love is part of what we mean by the 'life-instinct'. Love, however, can easily become converted into hatred. This, as common experience teaches, takes place in circumstances in which love has been blocked or frustrated. Homicidal acts are thus accounted for; and the same principle applies to suicide; it is due in many cases to the conversion of self-love into self-hatred.

But what is the explanation of this 'conversion' in circumstances in which love, directed to a proper love-object, does not become blocked or frustrated? This, apart from the possibility of insanity, is not easy to understand. The most common factor, however, is a complication of causes in which a sense of guilt is prominent. As already indicated in another connexion, where guilt is unconscious it sets up a need for punishment. This is the explanation of what is known as a 'self-immolation complex', as a result of which a person may starve himself to death, or attempt to do so. Suicide in such instances is only a more speedy and extreme way of meeting the need of the unconscious for atonement. Thus suicide often represents the death penalty pronounced on the self and carried out by the self.

The close relation between guilt, self-hatred and self-punishment is exemplified, not only in the tragic tale of Judas, but also in many a modern story of suicide, as a thorough sifting of the circumstances and motives which so often lead to it makes abundantly clear. Apart from the presence of guilt as a contributing factor in the explanation of suicide, there is evidence that so intolerable is life for some people that they find it easier to die than to continue to live. We recall that Job at one stage in his embittered experience decided that it would be better to end his life. We remember also the wistful words of the Psalmist: 'Oh that I had the wings of a dove, for then I would fly away and be at rest.' There are many devices to which people resort in their efforts to escape the unbearable hardships and sufferings of life. There is the use of narcotics and alcohol for this purpose; and many of our visualized day-dreams serve the same end. Some of these become morbid in the extreme, such as that of the woman who told me that there was a particular spot far out at sea into which she often pictured herself dropping unnoticed by anyone. There is, indeed, a form of religion which stresses the belief that no such thing as pain, sin, or death exists, these being regarded as only delusions of 'mortal mind'. Few, however, can indefinitely live out such a palpable falsehood. Then there is a variety of nervous symptoms, especially those of conversion-hysteria, through which many escape permanently from the harsh realities of life. Psychoanalysis contends that suicide often represents the unconscious desire, inherent in human nature, to return to the comfort and protection of the pre-natal condition in the mother's womb. Many dreams may be interpreted on the basis of this principle; but these theories seem far-fetched and are rejected by other schools of psychology.

Some who commit suicide would never have done so if they had not been told, by those whom they had consulted, that nothing more could be done for them, and that it was 'up to themselves'. Such statements should never be made to a depressed soul.

Many years ago I had this lesson brought home to me when a young man took his life in tragic circumstances. He had experienced an unhappy childhood in a home that had been abnormally repressive. He was never allowed to develop a real personality. Unfortunately, he married a woman who did not make things easier for him, though he looked forward in great hope to having a home with an atmosphere free from stress. The situation became complicated when in sheer despair he began an affair with another woman—a step which, although foolish and wrong, was in the circumstances easily understood. Inevitably this incident brought the punitive super-ego into action, with all the guilt and self-hatred which followed. Finally, the expiatory act, in suicide, brought to an end the unbearable mental torture through which for years he had been passing. We know that the night before the act was committed he telephoned his consultant to ascertain if anything further could be done for him. The answer was negative—that it was 'up to himself'.

Had this person, who was not psychotic, only opened his heart fully about his suicidal tendencies either to his doctor or minister, it is certain that he would have received the necessary preventative treatment. Large numbers of those who, although in the direst straits, have refused to give in, and finally have won through, were able to do so knowing that they had relatives and friends who would never lose faith in them, and who had pledged their support at no matter what cost.

EIGHT

Drugs and Religion

I begin this chapter, as is appropriate to do, by acknowledging my indebtedness to one of my many psychiatric friends, who has supplied me with the information here used regarding the various types of modern drugs and the purposes which these are intended to serve. It is hoped that ministers will not regard the facts here tabulated as wholly irrelevant to efficient pastoral work, particularly among the ailing in body or in mind.

First, however, it is well to comment on the widespread use of drugs, so characteristic of the age in which we live. More so than in any previous age people appear to find it necessary to fall back on the drug habit as a means of easing tension. Large numbers acknowledge that they could not carry on at all without such help. This fact has already been touched on in the chapter on 'The Problem of "Nerves"'. So far as the present-day treatment of non-physical illnesses is concerned, the tendency amongst psychiatrists appears to be to rely, more than formerly, on the use of drugs. We can understand this 'organic approach' to an appreciation of *psychotic* forms of illness and their treatment, for these are believed to be physically conditioned. Schizophrenia, for example, is seen to be due to some form of biochemical disturbance, and so is appropriately treated by selected drugs. So also are melancholia and hypomania. Other non-psychological methods which have beneficial results are electric convulsive shock therapy, and therapy based on the use of insulin. When it comes, however, to the treatment of nervous states by physical means, it is difficult to see how any real healing can take place from such treatments. One patient, for example, had received a form of 'sleep therapy' for many months without effect. He was suffering from acute anxiety symptoms which became worse instead of better under this form of treatment. Finally, not gaining any relief in this way, the patient sought help through simple psychological treatment. Soon the facts that lay at the root of his problem were brought to light. It had to do with wife-mother relationships—the usual conflict of loyalties, where both mother-in-law and daughter-in-law were jealous and possessive, and where life for the patient, as a consequence, had become intolerable. The home had been a constant centre of tension, worked up frequently into hysterical scenes during which the young man himself often collapsed. Now how could drug treatment possibly do more in this and similar situations, than ease the symptoms of anxiety?

However, despite the modern 'organic approach' to neurotic forms of illness and their treatment, most psychiatrists would agree that, along with the use of appropriate drugs, psycho-analytic procedures, in the effort to understand and treat nervous illnesses, simply cannot be ignored.

TYPES OF DRUG

The drugs most commonly in use at present in the treatment of mental and nervous patients are divided into three main categories: hypnotics or sedatives, tranquillizers, and anti-depressants.

(1) Hypnotics

These are sleep-producing drugs. They are, of course, like all other drugs in these three categories, procurable only through a doctor's prescription. One of these is known as amylobarbitone, six grains of which would produce sleep, while much smaller doses of the same drug given to an over-anxious patient will act as a sedative, removing anxiety but not inducing sleep.

The barbiturates are the most widely used hypnotics and sedatives. They are in the main harmless, although their frequent use may cause some risk of addiction.

(2) Tranquillizers

These, as the name implies, are intended to restrict over-anxiety and excitement. My psychiatric friend explains that these differ from hypnotics in that the latter affect the entire brain in its functioning, and so, if given in large enough doses, will produce a state of coma. People who are reported to have killed themselves with an overdose of drugs are usually those who have had access to these hypnotics. The effect of a tranquillizer, on the other hand, is selective in that it affects only some areas of the brain, and produces a soothing effect without in any way dulling one's intellectual faculties. Thus one can use these drugs, according to a doctor's directions, and at the same time easily carry out one's ordinary duties.

Perhaps the best-known of the tranquillizers is largactil. This has been much used in operations under local rather than general anaesthesia. It has been found to be very useful in controlling the abnormal behaviour and excitability of schizophrenics, and in subduing the panic which such patients are likely to experience when hallucinated.

It is largely through the judicious use of selected drugs of this kind that it has been possible to get rid of the 'padded cells' in mental hospitals, and to allow patients that measure of freedom which they now enjoy, and which undoubtedly has aided their recovery. These same drugs have made it possible greatly to extend the out-patients' treatment which is so much appreciated by people who, foolishly as we think, feel that a stigma is attached to those who have been treated as 'in-patients' in mental hospitals.

(3) Anti-depressants

These are drugs administered to deeply depressed patients. They act as a substitute for electric convulsive therapy. I gather, however, that although there is in use a wide variety of such drugs, psychiatrists are by no means agreed regardng their effectiveness. For one thing there are different forms of depression, so that the anti-depressant which may be beneficial in one case may be altogether ineffective, and even harmful, in another. But then the same facts apply to electric convulsive therapy. Some respond to this much more readily and completely than others. Therefore, further research must take place in this field before the medical profession can confidently treat depressed patients with anti-depressants. However, the measure of success already achieved in this area of treatment, limited and uncertain as it seems to be, gives promise of much further advance in this direction in the near future.

The matters which concern ministers more seriously than the points of general information about various types of drug and their functions, relate to specific religious problems. These may be put in the form of questions as follows: What theological implications of the effects of drugs on religious experience require consideration? To what extent, if any, is the physical and mental health of our people endangered through the use of drugs? Is their use consistent with Christian profession and practice?

THEOLOGICAL IMPLICATIONS

The effects of drugs on experience in general apply to religious experience in particular. One has only to visit a patient who is heavily drugged after an operation to become deeply impressed with the extent to which the physical can affect the mental, and even the spiritual, aspects of experience. Thus I recall that when one of my dearest friends in the ministry had contracted cancer of the stomach, and a most serious operation had to be performed in what proved to be an abortive attempt to save his life, I found him in a state of amazing spiritual ecstasy when I visited him. He had been treated with a massive dosage of a pain-killing drug. In his delirium he believed that he was engaged in the conduct of public worship in a large church, packed with an expectant congregation. He announced that I had come as the special guest preacher, and that immediately after the sermon had been preached a solo would be rendered by a notable singer, who also happened to be present in the room. I do not think that I ever witnessed a more happy death-bed scene. It took place only a few hours before he slipped peacefully into unconsciousness and passed away.

Now no one present could have had any illusions regarding the meaning and source of the patient's elation. He was 'in the seventh heaven', and although the experience had been produced by the special drug administered to him, yet it made his last hours radiantly happy, instead of distressing beyond endurance, which is what they undoubtedly would have been had no such drug been available.

This story raises important issues regarding the validity of religious experience. No one would deny that the reactions we have just described were artificially induced and were wholly subjective, and therefore 'invalid' in that sense. What, however, are we to make of intense forms of religious experience worked up also by artificial, albeit psychological, stimuli? (We have in mind the kind of religious behaviour discussed in the chapter on 'The Neurotic Elements in Religion'.) For we have seen that under powerful mass suggestion people became so completely passive and hypnoidal that the preacher could do whatever he willed with them. In this connexion reference might be made to an article written by the author of *Battle For The Mind*, and published in the *Spectator* of 21 May 1954, in which the following statement appears: 'John Wesley often produced, consciously or unconsciously, older versions of psychological and physiological shock therapies to religious ends.' He quotes Wesley himself as saying, 'How easy it is to suppose that strong, sudden and lively apprehension of the hideousness of sin and the wrath of God . . . should affect the body as well as the soul.' He further adds: 'Wesley often brought about physical effects by his preaching . . . which now seem extremely pertinent in view of the success of shock therapy in psychiatry. . . . The eighteenth century has been called "The Age Of Reason", but, paradoxically, it needed Wesley with his special techniques aimed at the emotions, to produce really dramatic changes in the outlook on life of the ordinary people of Great Britain. . . . The real danger is that such methods can be so overwhelmingly powerful in their effects as that they can be used to assist the forces of evil as well as of good.'

The question which these comments pose is: How far may we regard religious experience, produced under such stimuli and pressures, as at all valid? Now this word 'valid' is applied to religious matters in a variety of ways, as, for example, to the question of the 'validity' of certain ministries, or to the mode of conducting the sacraments. When we use it in connexion with religious conversion, or spiritual experience, we raise the question as to the criteria of validity. Already it has been suggested that what is purely subjective, individualistic, and artificially stimulated is not valid, in the sense that it is not real, although real enough to the person who is the subject of the experience. Simpler criteria of validity are: Whether the particular religious experience we are considering is or is not consistent with *corporate* Christian experience, and whether it is producing appropriate fruits in the life. These, indeed, were the tests of religious reality which had impressed Wesley himself; for, great evangelist that he was, he understood the difference between a genuine Christian experience and forms of religious experience that lacked the qualities of true Christian saintliness. As Dr Sargant acknowledged in his article in the *Spectator*: 'Only one great religious leader has succeeded in altering the face of England in a generation, and that was John Wesley.'

The philosophical problem closely connected with that of the validity of religious experience is one that is bound to exercise the minds of doctors themselves, namely the ancient one of body-mind relationships, and the bearing of this on such doctrines as that of immortality. Some Christian doctors have suggested to me that they need more help than we ministers provide in the solution of some of their own theological problems. Conditioned as they are by their special training to give priority to bodily functioning in body-mind relationships, how can they believe that once the brain disintegrates, as it does at death, there can be anything left to survive? At least part of the answer to this is that there is as much evidence for the power of mind over matter as for that of matter over mind. The psychology of suggestion is a sufficient refutation of the view that the traffic between these entities is a one-way affair. Moreover, the analogy of the radio set, used by C. S. Lewis and quoted with approval in *Christian Essays In Psychiatry* (p. 20), is suggestive. Lewis likens the body and mind to a radio set, itself a complicated piece of mechanism, tuned to receive a programme. The set is essentially material. The programme, on the other hand, is essentially immaterial. Yet the programme provides the ultimate justification for the existence of the set; and it is to receive and give expression to the programme, that the set has been designed and built. None the less if the set has become damaged or decayed it is quite likely to distort the programme, even to the point at which interference renders it no longer recognizable. When this occurs the *set* needs attention, although to the superficial listener it may appear that it is the programme which has gone wrong.

This analogy should be carried further to meet the special point we have in mind—that of clarifying our thoughts in regard to the possibility of the persistence of the self after bodily death. Supposing the set is damaged, or has decayed beyond repair, does this affect the programme? Has the programme ceased to exist? Obviously not, as a new set if switched on will very quickly show. In fact the programme will come through all the more clearly because a new, and more perfect, set has been provided. The implications of this for the Christian doctrine of the Resurrection require no explanation or elaboration.

The second problem to which the use of drugs gives rise is one relating to health and morals.

The use of drugs, under strict medical supervision, is, of course, indispensable. For example, a great variety of new drugs for combating disease is now in use. These are called antibiotics. Many drugs, as already indicated, are pain-killing. Without their help human beings could not endure the suffering caused by some forms of disease. But the *indiscriminate* use of drugs is dangerous to health; and even where these are used under the direction of doctors there are side-effects which sometimes issue in consequences more tragic than the disease it-self. Indeed, according to the medical profession itself, many drugs have been insufficiently tested. This has been brought much into the open through the discovery that the use of thalidomide drugs by expectant mothers can be the cause of serious abnor-malities in their children. We remember in this connexion the world-wide interest aroused by the trial of a Swiss mother and her doctor who had 'put to sleep' an infant whose deformity was attributed to this cause, and who had done so obviously out of compassion for the child. The wealth of sympathy felt for the woman was evident in the spontaneous outburst of cheering when her acquittal was announced in the court.

Not only are some drugs dangerous from the standpoint of health, but even more so from that of morals. For example, many drugs are habit-forming, and can render an addict as helpless and hopeless as the most pitiable alcoholic. Even barbiturates can give rise to some risk of this kind; but they have no serious side-effects.

It is when we come to narcotics proper, and especially to the illegal traffic to which they give rise, that the danger becomes acute. These have not been referred to earlier in this chapter because they are in a class by themselves. Cocaine, opium, and heroin are amongst the best known of these. Cocaine is extracted from the coca plant grown mainly in Bolivia and Peru. Opium comes from poppies; and as China is the land of poppies it is also the main source of opium. This product has brought to the Chinese very considerable revenue. Because it is a prohibited drug it sells at competitive prices—more than £5 per ounce. Heroin is a much more powerful narcotic than either of the other two; when it gets into the hands of the trafficker it can fetch almost any price from a wealthy but desperate addict. The agents for these narcotics are members of highly-organized 'dope rings' scattered all over the world. They earn colossal sums, many of them becoming millionaires.

The third problem connected with the use of drugs is one felt acutely by some sensitive and scrupulous types of Christian. The minister may find in his congregation some who worry about taking a pill, even when it is prescribed by the doctor. Some patients in mental hospitals resist medication through fear of being deliberately poisoned in this way by their 'enemies'. The over-conscientious Christian does so because he thinks it quite wrong for Christians to resort to such artificial means of inducing peace of mind, when prayer ought fully to meet their needs.

These folk require some instruction in the ways by which God answers our prayers. Thus people troubled in this respect may be reminded that perhaps God has been answering their prayers by some means unrecognized by them, as, for example, by making available new drugs suited to their needs. By this procedure they should be helped to feel that the particular tablet prescribed is a gift of God to them, and to similar sufferers. It would also be well to ask these over-scrupulous Christians, who are hesitant to do what their doctor advises in the matter of medication, to dwell on the tremendous benefits which many of these drugs have brought to mankind. Perhaps such a story as that connected with the discovery of strepto-mycin should be related by the pastor, either to one whom he meets in his pastoral rounds, and who is in spiritual doubt over this problem: better still, to the entire congregation which in this way might be instructed regarding the benefits of selected drugs, by using the following story as an illustration. In any case, a summary of the main facts connected with this remarkable statement will be an appropriate conclusion to this chapter.

The discoverer of this drug was a Russian called Waksman—at least he was born a Russian, but emigrated in his boyhood years to the United States. He became a student at the state Agricultural College at Rutgers, New Jersey. He interested himself in the study of the soil, believing that there is much more in a blob of clay than mere dirt. 'Each spoonful of dirt was for him a world with a population of hundreds of millions of living organisms. Under his microscope the dirt burst into life as rich, colourful and violent as the jungle,' wrote Richard Carter in an article on Waksman in *Life* magazine. Waksman isolated and catalogued groups of microbes discovered by him in this fashion. The search went on for very many years—a marvellous venture of faith. In 1940 he discovered the first actinomycin, an organism which he believed provided the richest source of antibiotic organisms so far known. He found, however, that this organism killed not only the disease-creating bacteria, but also the animals on which it was tried. Then, in 1943, he extracted, from two strains of the original antibiotic, another powerful one which had none of the toxic effects of the first. This discovery has had miraculous results in controlling whooping-cough, typhoid, cholera, pneumonia, and tuberculosis. In the article to which we have referred, Richard Carter, speaking about the persistence of this great scientist over the years in concentrating on blobs of soil in the hope of finding the required organism, said: 'The feat was comparable to finding five needles, one of pure gold, while picking through an infinite number of haystacks.'

Of course Waksman became tremendously wealthy, and the firm of chemists that had perfected the drug was making thereby profits running into millions. This embarrassed Waksman, who felt that his disinterested love of discovery for the benefits and blessings of the human race was being threatened. So he persuaded the firms to allow other companies also to produce the drug. Most of his own money Waksman gave to the founding of a school of microbiology. To secure his services he was offered fabulous salaries by some of the wealthiest universities in America; but in sheer loyalty to his own college in New Jersey he resisted every such offer. Referring to the way in which streptomycin has saved children suffering from tubercular meningitis (a disease that formerly was fatal), Waksman himself said: 'I have been embraced by children whose lives have been spared in this way; not only so, but by their mothers and even by their physicians. Could there be any greater reward for me?'

You will agree, I think, that a story like this should help to show how, through such discoveries, God has answered the prayers of Christians down the generations for the healing of disease; so it is not a matter of either prayer or drugs, but usually of both.

NINE

Some Moral Disorders

In the preceding pages consideration was given to the typical symptoms of the main neuroses and psychoses, so that ministers might be able to recognize these, assess their seriousness, and hence refer those affected for appropriate treatment. We now turn our attention to a different type of problem, namely, to certain disorders the symptoms of which primarily affect the character and behaviour of some who are committed to our care. By the very nature of their trouble, people afflicted in these ways are, in the first instance, much more likely to seek the help of their minister than that of the doctor; and much of his time and energy may have to be devoted to straightening out the various tangles in which such people often find themselves. Indeed, it is generally when their behaviour has landed them in trouble with the police that they or their relatives look to the minister for help. Often in such circumstances the minister will find himself in the law courts pleading their cause —that is if he understands that they are to be regarded as patients of a certain type rather than as deliberate wrongdoers. So some understanding of legal procedures, as well as of psychological principles, will be found useful in effective pastoral practice.

We shall select for consideration four of the most common types of moral disorder with which ministers will find themselves confronted from time to time. It is important that these should be understood as far as possible, and that the right method of dealing with them be adopted.

ALCOHOLISM

This subject has come into the very forefront of both psychiatric and pastoral concern in recent years. This is largely due to the work being done in mental hospitals for alcoholic patients, and to statistics now available regarding the prevalence of alcoholic addiction in every community and country. It is due primarily, however, to the splendid work accomplished by Alcoholics Anonymous—a movement which was founded in the United States more than thirty years ago and is now well established all over the world. Ministers should make themselves familiar with the principles on which A.A., as it has come to be known, is based. These are called the 'Twelve Steps of the A.A. Recovery Programme'; and here they are as expressed by recovered alcoholics themselves:

(1) We admitted we were powerless over alcohol; that our lives had become unmanageable.

(2) Came to believe that a power greater than ourselves could restore us to sanity.

(3) Made a decision to turn our will and our lives over to the care of God *as we understood Him.*

(4) Made a searching and fearless moral inventory of ourselves.

(5) Admitted to God, to ourselves, and to another human being the exact nature of our wrongs.

(6) Were entirely ready to have God remove all these defects of character.

(7) Humbly asked Him to remove our shortcomings.

(8) Made a list of all persons we had harmed and became willing to make amends to them all.

(9) Made direct amends to such people wherever possible, except when to do so would injure them or others.

(10) Continued to take personal inventory, and when we were wrong, promptly admitted it.

(11) Sought through prayer and meditation to improve our conscious contact with God *as we understood Him*, praying only for knowledge of His will for us and the power to carry that out.

(12) Having had a spiritual awakening as the result of these steps, we tried to carry this message to alcoholics, and practise these principles in all our affairs.

This programme is very searching, though simple, and it is obvious that there are a few of the rules which are particularly important. One is that nothing can be done for an alcoholic who does not give evidence of a sincere determination to renounce drink and to do so once and for all. Secondly, he must realize that he cannot do this in his own strength, but through Divine help. He must hand over his life to the care of

God, as God is understood by members of Alcoholics Anonymous. He must face facts about himself and those whom he has wronged and put the wrongs right as far as this is possible. This means that he must stop blaming others for the plight in which he finds himself. He must seek to rescue others who are alcoholics and who desire to reform; and he must go after those who may have lapsed. These principles of A.A. remind us of those which have been in use in some churches for years in programmes of evangelism; and John Wesley's 'class-meetings' had many features similar to the 'experience' meetings of A.A., for his converts (many of whom had been alcoholics) encouraged one another in faith and life, and were urged to keep before themselves an inventory of their own faults.

Perhaps the most painful factors in the day-to-day life of alcoholics is their sense of utter loneliness and deep inferiority. The pathos of their condition in these respects was brought home to me many years ago; for, working as a young minister in the heart of an industrial city, I was brought into close contact with many of them. I then began, once each week, to visit their drinking haunts, where I sat for long hours listening to them, and in this way learning much about the psychology of alcoholism.

I sometimes remained all night in a common lodging-house observing the behaviour of those who made such places their shelters; for having been deserted by their friends and relatives they had no real homes. Of course I talked to as many of them as was possible, seeking to elicit information regarding the background of their lives, and the reasons for their desertion and loneliness. I found that many of them were subjects of acute inferiority which I discovered to be one factor in the causation of alcoholism. Thus at the door of one public house stood a man who was offering a welcome to everyone who entered, and who was assuring the unemployed among them of a job at a certain wage. I went into this person's social condition afterwards to find that he himself had been without work for over two years. At that time it appeared obvious to me that none of these true alcoholics really craved for drink as such, but rather for the oblivion which intoxicants induce, and for the sense of well-being which they could derive through the flight from reality into a world of pure fantasy. It also came home to me with real force that unemployment is more than a social cancer—it is as well a grievous moral wrong for which liberal unemployment allowances are not an answer.

The use of intoxicants as a narcotic is only one form of drinking; so the pastor should keep in mind the various categories into which this indulgence can be classified.

There is, to begin with, moderate or social drinking. It is most difficult to convince the majority of people today—including churchgoers—that there is anything wrong in this. Indeed, drinking at present is so prominent in radio and television programmes that it is impossible for impressionable teenagers not to feel that no social function can be complete without it. Drink, however, is not often explicitly mentioned in these programmes; but what is called 'subliminal suggestion' is very evident; and this is much more powerful as a 'conditioner' than any direct recommendation of the delights of wine or spirits. For one thing, it has caused an impression to be registered deeply in viewers, as well as in participants, that no one can really be mature who is a total abstainer. How then can a minister persuade his young people to abstain? He cannot convince them of the importance of this by elaborating on the ravages caused by drink; but he can impress those with open minds on the subject by referring to the warnings issued by magistrates, judges, doctors, and police, of the dangers of even moderate drinking among those who own and drive cars, and, therefore, who have the lives of others in their hands. Furthermore—and this I personally find to be seldom satisfactorily answered—no one who begins merely as a social drinker ever intends to be anything else; yet a large percentage of those who indulge in moderation turn out to be alcoholics. Here the symptoms of the alcoholic, and his helplessness, should be elaborated. Indeed no congregation should be left without an occasional lecture on the subject given by some psychiatrist or other expert.

The second category to which drinkers may belong is that of the so-called drunks. These commence as social drinkers; but the habit grows on them, and they drink to excess simply because they want to do so. Hadfield speaks of such as people with 'brutish' natures. They drink because they want to; and they *could* give it up but have no will to do so.

Then there are the alcoholics proper. Drinking with these is not an indulgence which they enjoy. It is a *disease*; and this is the fact, above all others, which the minister should keep in mind in his pastoral activities among the relatives of alcoholics. These and their neighbours think of alcoholics in terms of people who are 'no good', or moral weaklings, or people without any sense of shame. This is how they are described by relatives, and such an approach to them can have only one effect, namely to undermine still further their sense of self-respect and deepen their feelings of inferiority, thus rendering their condition still more hopeless.

I have found another classification of excessive drinkers to be useful. There is a difference between the chronic alcoholic and the dipsomaniac. The former, as indicated, seeks through intoxication a way of escape from the severities and stresses of life. Unlike the common 'drunk' he is of a hypersensitive nature. The latter, on the other hand, periodically goes on the 'binge'. Normally he indulges in spirits and is inclined to drink in solitude. His 'bouts' may continue only for a couple of days, or they may be prolonged even for months. Meanwhile his business duties are seriously interrupted. Posts of responsibility are taken from him. He may lose his job altogether and ultimately find himself among the denizens of the underworld. In my wanderings into public houses and hostels where disowned people find nightly shelter, I came across some professional men, and many who at one time were responsible business executives. Between the drinking 'bashes' these men, unlike the typical alcoholic, lose all craving for drink. Indeed they hate it and feel abnormally self-confident about being able to 'go straight' in the future. Not long afterwards, however, the typical symptoms return. These include moods of depression, 'nerviness', and apprehensiveness, as well as a tendency to evade those who can help them. All these are infallible signs of the imminence of a further 'attack'; so these hapless people disappear and are usually discovered in some solitary place such as in a hotel room, and always in a drunken coma. When they recover, they are full of remorse, and will contact their minister to intercede with their relatives on their behalf. They usually insist that they have no memory of anything that happened in the interval. They seem to suffer from 'blackouts' so far as their behaviour during the drinking periods is concerned.

Why do the symptoms of alcoholism and dipsomania differ in pattern? This is not easily answered. It is suggested, however, that the latter belong to the class to which the name cyclothymic applies. It is well known that, as earlier indicated, some people are so constituted—notably manic-depressives. These pass through cycles of mood, one of which is painful depression, the onset of which cannot easily be accounted for. Perhaps dipsomaniacs represent some of those who are of this type, and who, at times, undergo periods of acute depression. It is when the onset of such a mood is imminent that the victim seeks a way of escape in a bout of excessive drinking. Thus, for the dipsomaniac, the taking of alcohol may have a drug-like effect.

Fuller appreciation of the causes of dipsomania may reveal a history of repressed emotions which goes back to childhood. One pathetic case comes to my mind in this connexion. It is that of a gifted 'celebrity' who manifested from time to time all the reactions of the dipsomaniac. The early symptoms of an onset were general apprehension and dread. During this stage in the development of the usual symptoms her pet dog and cat, she said, seemed to become enemies. So did even the flowers in her garden. From an environment charged in this way with fear, she usually sought escape by one expedient. She handed over the keys of her flat to her doctor (who was a lady), and retired to her bedroom after having provided for herself many bottles of spirits and gin. She passed quickly into a state of perfect peace and well-being through liberal indulgence in these. When asked to describe her feelings while under the influence of drink she said, 'It was as though my brain had been padded round with rich, black satin.' Asked for associations with this, she said that it reminded her of mother-love. This resulted in the recall of early memories of the bitterest kind, when her mother died and her father married again. Unfortunately, her stepmother was a sadist of the most vicious kind, who often whipped the child unmercifully when the latter had been prepared to take her bath. This often resulted in the child screaming for her own mother, and for the comfort which only a real mother could provide for her child. How perfectly the unconscious mind typified the comforts of mother-love in the soft, rich, satin feeling!

The question is often asked, 'Can alcholism be cured?' The usual answer made by alcoholics themselves is that this is not possible in any absolute sense. Once a person becomes an alcoholic he is always an alcoholic. What is meant, however, is that he is always a potential alcoholic patient. To maintain sobriety he has strictly to observe such rules as A.A., for example, lays down. At first it is necessary to enquire what are the steps to be taken to ensure the removal of the symptoms and secure the measure of adjustment to himself and to life which will enable him once more to take his place as a normal member of society.

Since there is usually a number of factors—organic, psychological, sociological, and personal—involved in alcoholic disorders, the permanent alleviation of symptoms is no simple task. The pastor concerned with the problem should realize that the rehabilitation of any such patient is a combined operation. First, the services of the doctor should be called in, and the patient must be willing to undergo a course of 'aversion therapy' in hospital. This is the first step towards recovery, and, fortunately, the conscience of the community is now so much more enlightened regarding the nature of alcoholism, and the needs of alcoholic patients, that separate hospitals suitable for their treatment are being established in every large city. Secondly, since many take refuge in excessive drinking from the disappointments and frustrations of life, psychiatry is essential side by side with medical treatment. Thirdly, since alcoholics must know that they cannot reform themselves by sheer will power, as can the ordinary 'drunk', they will need spiritual therapy which will include a complete surrender of themselves to God, and a reliance on His help. Here in particular is where the work of the pastor becomes important. Finally, these patients desperately need understanding and encouragement from the Church and community—as well as from A.A.

It will not do, as we have already stated, to denounce these sufferers as delinquents, or to urge them to pull themselves together. This they cannot do any more than others whose behaviour is compulsive. Such advice, indeed, can only have one result, namely, to drive them further into the depths of despair. All alcoholics need friendship, fellowship, and encouragement. It is because they find these through A.A. that this movement has been so beneficial. But the Christian Church should at least be as effective as A.A. in dealing with its own members who have succumbed to this disease.

Once an alcoholic has been restored to society, and to a measure of independence, he must undertake never again to touch drink if security against regression, or relapse, is to be guaranteed. Alcoholics themselves know, as well as dipsomaniacs, that to take one glass at a social function is at once to become 'automatic', and so the whole process of reclamation has to commence over again. Those who have been alcoholics tell us that even the smell of intoxicants can send a potential patient back into alcoholic despair. Hence the importance of ministers considering whether it is wise to make use of fermented wine in the administration of the Holy Communion to alcoholics. This matter has exercised the minds of ministers whose Churches have had a tradition in this respect, and who are unwilling to use unfermented wine instead. They have advised that alcoholics who seek spiritual help through the Holy Communion should partake only of one element, leaving the wine untouched. This, however, is not an ideal solution to the problem, since even the smell of the wine as the minister passes the chalice in front of them may be sufficient to reactivate the craving. Besides, to pass them over will be noticed by others; and this will be embarrassing for the particular communicant who is usually over-sensitive. It would seem, therefore, that the only effective solution to this problem is to substitute for all communicants, unfermented, instead of fermented wine. Why this should be regarded as rendering 'ineffective' or less 'valid', this means of grace, it is difficult to understand.

COMPULSIVE GAMBLING

Although the incidence of *compulsive* gambling is not so widespread as that of alcoholism it is much more difficult to deal with. One reason for this is that whilst alcoholism has been the subject of careful study by expert psychologists, and whilst curative centres have been set up to deal with the problem on a scientific and spiritual basis, comparable attention to the nature and results of compulsive gambling is still in its infancy. Up to the present, for the most part, this study has been approached from the standpoint of social ethics rather than from that of psychiatry. It is only now that students of the subject are beginning to look upon it as a form of *disease*, in all respects comparable to other forms of compulsive behaviour. Even still the general public tend to regard the compulsive gambler as a 'no-good'—a weak and degenerate type of individual to be scorned rather than considered as a patient in dire need of understanding, sympathy and, treatment.

It is right that ministers should call attention to the vast sums of money that are being wasted on this form of 'sport', whilst more than half the world's population is in a state of semi-starvation. The very considerable sums which 'fortunate' gamblers have gained in this way have, up to the present, not even been included in income for purposes of taxation, although capital gains tax is seen to be a reasonable source of revenue. The proposal to levy a modest tax on such gambling gains is at least a step in the right direction.

Some exponents of Christian ethics,[1] we find, hold the view that gambling is justifiable as a form of entertainment so long as the stakes are small. Only gambling with large amounts which the gambler in fact cannot afford is, in their judgement, unethical. But what we have already said regarding moderate drinking—that no alcoholic ever intended to be anything else than a 'social' drinker—applies also to gambling; but then no one knows who is a *potential* compulsive gambler or who is likely to become a pathetic alcoholic.

Not being aware of the distress caused by compulsive gambling, or even of the difference between gambling as a disease, and 'social' gambling as a form of entertainment, many church members become quite impatient over any apparently 'puritanical' approach to this problem by ministers. They argue, not without some point, that there is no difference between gambling on the race course or in a bingo hall, and gambling on the stock exchange. But there is surely a difference between speculating on the stock market—especially with borrowed money—and investing in selected industrials and

[1] For example Herbert Waddams in *A New Introduction To Moral Theology*.

equities which is obviously beneficial to the economy of the country.

Such points as we have made thus far may stimulate a healthy debate on the whole subject in church discussion groups. In this connexion a rational approach to the problem rather than denunciation, on the traditional lines, or an authoritative laying down of the law, is the only one likely to succeed in the present religious and ethical climate.

It is, however, to the *disease* of gambling and to its psychology, that we must give attention in the remainder of this chapter, for it is in attempts to deal with the compulsive gambler and with his distressed relatives and dependants that the minister often finds himself most helpless. So let us suggest some respects in which pastoral aid may prove beneficial.

First, it is important that the minister should become specially concerned with the gambler himself rather than with the nature of his 'vice', and that—for purposes of gaining the person's confidence, without which he cannot help to any extent—he should not begin with any criticisms of the man's behaviour, but empathetically place himself at the side of the patient, and try to appreciate his predicament.

Secondly, having established a suitable rapport with the person, he should invite him to unburden his mind, and he should encourage him to give expression to every relevant detail, without showing the least signs of impatience or condemnation. In this connexion ministers should realize that they learn most regarding compulsive gambling from the gambler himself rather than from books on the subject—even if such were available.

Thirdly, having gained the man's confidence the minister should continue the interview by putting some leading questions to him. The purpose of this procedure would be to enable the gambler himself to get a full picture of the realities of the situation. That this is essential becomes clear when we remember that gambling, as a compulsive craze, no less than alcoholic addiction, can obscure the real issues and dangers to which the gambling addict is exposed.

Amongst leading questions designed to clarify the situation for the gambler himself should be:

(1) How in your case did the gambling craze commence? Can you recall the circumstances in which you began to bet? Most likely there will come, in reply, a long story regarding initial small bets in school, and the encouragement to indulge by other boys.

(2) He should next enquire regarding the attitude of the parents when they discovered that their boy was being influenced in this way. Perhaps this may elicit information regarding the beginnings of petty stealing from parents and other schoolboys, so as to satisfy the new interest. This, rather than the betting habit itself, may be the cause of the parents' anger and punishment of the boy—an attitude which the gambler himself confesses only made him more determined to continue the indulgence. On the other hand, there may come the story of a different parental attitude, such as one compulsive gambler explained when he said his father often sent him along 'to put money on the dogs, so as to entertain myself'. This same person—now a compulsive gambler—had misappropriated considerable sums of money from his employers simply to satisfy his craving.

(3) A further question may be put to the gambler at this stage—What have been the effects of gambling on your character and personality? Try, in answering this, to compare your character and major interests now with what these were before this indulgence became compulsive. Most likely this will cause the patient to become aware of a steady hardening of his feelings and attitudes, and a confession that the pain he is causing to his relatives never worries him. Here the compulsive gambler is a greater problem than the subject of any other compulsive behaviour, such as the alcoholic, who at least has periods of intense self-loathing, as has also the kleptomaniac.

(4) Continuing this kind of probing, the minister may ask, more specifically, what effect his compulsion has on his honesty and truthfulness? This should lead to confessions regarding attempts on the part of the addict to secure money by a series of well-thought-out stories, as, for example, that a friend had borrowed from him a considerable amount of money promising to repay it in the course of days when an insurance policy was about to mature. He may also add that his friend has let him

down, and that, as a matter of fact, he himself had been foolish enough to go as guarantor to the bank for his friend, and that now the bank was pressing him for the amount. If he fails to meet his liability within a week, the bank, he alleges, will publicize the facts in the press. He pleas for help, particularly because his wife is unaware of his predicament and should the facts be divulged she would either collapse nervously or desert him. We may depend on it that the entire story is a fabrication and that the fact is that he himself has got himself into a financial mess through gambling.

(5) When all this has come home to the gambler himself, further questions should be directed to the motives behind the gambler's addiction. Here the matter of covetousness, expressing itself in the endeavour to gain large sums without any equivalent in work, may be a relevant point. This is likely, however, to be only the initial motive which influences all forms of gambling. When the indulgence becomes a disease then the motive may be the interest or excitement stimulated by the 'game' itself. When, however, the gambler finds himself in financial difficulties, gambling becomes a compulsion simply in the hope of winning, and thus being able to rehabilitate himself in the life of his family.

On the positive side, one of the main duties of the pastor should be to help the patient to regain a measure of self-respect. No one who has completely lost respect for himself can even begin to help himself. But how can one regain faith in oneself? Here both the alcoholic and the compulsive gambler will be encouraged to some extent if they are assured that the minister does not regard them as 'no-goods', but as patients in need of treatment. Then the pastor's duty will be to induce relatives to adopt a similar attitude of positive encouragement and helpfulness. Then, if they are convinced that the person is sincere in his determination to overcome his disability, they should help—even at some risk of disappointment—to solve the problems to which gambling has given rise. Failure to do so means that anxiety still fills the man's mind and, as in the case of the alcoholic, there will remain a temptation, and probably a compulsion, to escape from his unhappiness in another 'bout' of betting and gambling.

Next, the man should be urged to come into some form of

Christian fellowship—preferably into church clubs, to join in recreational activities in which he would find friends who would encourage him and in this way build up still further his sense of self-respect.

'Gamblers Anonymous' has, as yet, not become established in every community as has 'Alcoholics Anonymous', but ministers could render a genuine service by taking the initiative in organizing such an institution in their areas. For, of course, the sharing of experience by those who have suffered in the same way will prove much more satisfying and curative than membership in a fellowship of those who know nothing from personal experience of the intensity of the gambler's craving, or of the utter hopelessness of the situations in which these patients find themselves.

Nor should the Church fail to realize the possibilities of a total change of life for compulsive gamblers through religious conversion. On this the *British Medical Journal* in an issue in 1956 stated: 'In religious conversion the complete upheaval which takes place in the emotional life is capable of curing various forms of neurosis, alcoholism, and other forms of functional disorder, apparently by removing the causative factors which contribute so largely to the neurotic temperament. The patient thus achieves a peace of mind and contentment, which to a large extent removes the effects of stress and strain. Conversion operates mainly through a change of will and motive, and by giving the patient a personal faith that God can satisfy his deepest needs, furnishes him with an adequate purpose in life and supports him in adversity.'

This applies as much to compulsive gambling as to alcoholism and other forms of moral disease. It is our opinion, however, that the religious approach to such problems should be made after psychiatric and psychological treatment has clarified the mind of the patient in regard to the realities of the situation, and the motives involved are laid bare and self-respect and hope are restored. Otherwise, a situation may develop in which the force of religious suggestion simply results in the replacement of one set of symptoms and compulsions for another, and the last state may become at least as unsatisfactory as the first.

SOME SEXUAL DEVIATIONS

So much has been written on sexual matters in recent years, and there has been such a widespread dissemination of knowledge regarding the facts of life through radio and television discussion, that only the briefest treatment of some of the most important aspects of the subject is necessary here.

First, notwithstanding the more candid and open discussions of sexual matters with which we are now familiar, large numbers continue to be the subjects of acute guilt feelings arising not merely from sexual perversions, but simply from the awareness of sex desires. This somehow causes considerable distress to those who unconsciously equate sexual feeling with wickedness. The history of religion itself, strangely enough, suggests two reasons for this misunderstanding. One is the continuance, mainly unconscious, of the Gnostic heresy of the essentially evil nature of matter and hence of all bodily functioning. This influence is largely accountable for the double standard of Christian saintliness which we encounter in some types of traditional moral theology. Thus, for example, the celibate life is regarded in this brand of ascetic theology as much more saintly and meritorious than that of the ordinary Christian (whose life is often much more sacrificial).

There is also in some types of religion a lingering puritanical influence which affects peoples' attitude to the sexual factor. Thus we still encounter parents who speak of sexual desire as an element to be rigorously repressed as in itself sinful, and not even to be discussed. This attitude inevitably results in conflicts and in a fundamental cleavage of one's personality, and it is in this that the deviations and perversions we are to consider here have their origin. What is even more serious is that this false attitude to sexual feeling accounts, as has already been explained, for some neurotic symptoms and even for the unchristlike religion so common in many quarters.

But let us concentrate our attention on the guilt-producing perversions which will bring many of our people to us in confession or in bewilderment.

Auto-eroticism

This term is a combination of the Greek words *autos* meaning 'self' and *eros*, one of several Greek terms, usually translated by the word 'love'. So auto-eroticism refers to a habit in which solitary sexual indulgence takes place. This gives rise to intense physical pleasure, but is usually followed—especially in sensitive people—by considerable self-loathing.

Freudians have shown that some parts of the body, when stimulated, give rise to much more intense sensations than others. These they name 'erogenous zones'. This is why children, at a surprisingly early age, appear to find pleasure in exploring their own bodies. When in this process the genital regions become involved, parents, under the impression that this is infantile masturbation, punish the child or at any rate scold him; but in so doing they create in the mind of the child a premature sense of guilt. This should be avoided at all costs, for it makes for unhappiness and morbidity at a stage in a child's development when it is important that he should accept himself *in toto*, and be as free as possible from guilt and fear. The parents, of course, misunderstand the child's behaviour which has nothing to do with sexuality in any proper sense. Even Freudians would agree with this. The behaviour is little more than the discovery of a general pleasurable sensation through self-exploration. If, however, there is evidence of a fixation of attention on any part of the body, especially on the reproductive organs, then the simplest and least harmful method of dealing with the situation is for the parent to remove the child's hand quietly and without smacking or scolding him.

In adolescence, masturbation, as a *perversion*, is so common as to be almost universal, and it affects both sexes. No wonder that Freudians connect this practice—for many so guilt-creating—with the incidence of religious conversion, pointing out, indeed, that conversion is mainly 'an adolescent phenomenon'. Many adolescents who come to make confession to us are found to be most penitential over this indulgence which, they say, has become compulsive. They confess that their wills are powerless to deal with their problem. They have tried and failed so often that they are in despair. I myself have always regarded any sexual deviation as a symptom of frustration and a failure properly to sublimate this energy, but psychologists of the standing of Dr J. H. Hadfield speak of 'sexual neuroses', and this seems reasonable as a description of those in whom any sexual perversion is a compulsion which is beyond their ability to control. One cause of a sexual neurosis in the sense in which we are now considering it is a serious lack of fondling by the mother, or a complete deprivation of mother love. Thus it is a compensatory reaction. I have found this explanation helpful when dealing with those whose spirits are clouded in this way.

To exaggerate the physical or mental ill-effects of solitary sexual indulgence is often an important factor in the causation of anxiety neurosis. We have traced the origin of such symptoms on more than one occasion to the onset of a traumatic experience which results from the reading of a badly-written 'purity pamphlet'. Thus one university student decided to withdraw from university courses and devote his time to prayer and meditation in preparation for the end which, according to the pamphlet which he had read, would not be long delayed. Actually when he came for an interview he was already looking for the ominous symptoms. Admittedly, few nowadays take masturbation as much to heart as this. The majority of those who indulge—and it is said that ninety per cent of adolescents actually do so—have no compunction at all over the matter. Yet there is a minimum of young, and also middle-aged people, in whom compulsions take this form and they require, and will seek, pastoral help.

Masturbation, however, when practised by those who are to any extent religiously scrupulous has harmful effects in that it undermines their sense of self-respect, and results in an unhealthy self-fixation. As implied, too, in the chapter on 'The Neurotic Element in Religion' this habit can be a factor in the onset (through a 'psychological conversion' which consists mainly in the inhibiting of the indulgence and the repression of guilt to which the indulgence gave rise) of a form of religious fanaticism.

Sadism and Masochism

Sadism and masochism constitute a pair of opposite morbid trends much less common than the perversion we have been considering. They are to be understood as reactions into adulthood of impulses that are natural in childhood. They become perversions when sexual satisfaction is derived from them and they become substitute satisfactions for normal sexual experience.

Sadism, so-called from the Marquis de Sade, who practised what he preached, represents the intense satisfaction people find in inflicting pain on others. The extent to which it prevails in human nature becomes obvious in crises such as war or revolution when latent sadistic tendencies burst into the most cruel forms of behaviour. It comes to the surface also in mob hysteria, when, under a sadistic leader, people surrender to the most diabolical acts of terrorism in which their opponents become brutally tortured. If sadism were not so deeply rooted in human nature the horrors of the German concentration camps could never have taken place. And there is much evidence for the fact that, in sublimated form, this cruel streak affects, more or less, most people. Hence the amount of rationalizing in regard to cruel sports, including the stag hunt, the Spanish bull rings, and the popularity of boxing. Pain also can be inflicted on others psychologically rather than physically. There are individuals—and many of them are in the Christian Church—who seem to take a delight in hurting fellow church members by the bitter word and unfair gossip. The same element in human nature finds expression in the satire that renders some television programmes so popular. Are the varied expressions of sadism not sufficient evidence of 'original sin' in human nature? It is so deep-seated that its evidence, in sublimated form, is unmistakable even in those who claim to be 'entirely sanctified'. But then, not even our great evangelists are aware of the need for that radical transformation of human nature which turns cruelty, sublimated or unsublimated, into tenderness, and hatred into love.

Masochism, from an Austrian named Sascher-Masoch, means the opposite of sadism. It is the trend which finds satisfaction in self-flagellation. In its pronounced form it becomes a substitute for normal sexual activity. Thus is explained the fact that in most large cities there are hidden centres where masochism, as a perversion, is practised, but much less attention is called to this than to ordinary brothels. Sublimated masochism manifests itself, as does sadism, in a variety of ways, as for example in the patient who 'enjoys bad health', or, indeed, in the morbid delight with which some of the early martyrs went to their deaths—or is this too fantastic? In his *Pastoral Psychology and Mental Health* (p. 257) Dr J. R. Oliver writes, 'The masochistic man wants to be dominated by some cruel woman; he wants her to maltreat him, to put her booted foot on his neck, to hold him in absolute subjection. Many so-called henpecked husbands are of this type; they are henpecked because they like it.'

It should be kept in mind by ministers that only when sadists or masochists are in desperation will they seek interviews or look for help. Not understanding the origin of their trouble they become guilty and ashamed, and will keep their conflicts and temptations to themselves as long as possible. Nor must it be supposed that sadists and masochists cannot be sincere Christians. Thus one man who for years had been a missionary teacher felt finally compelled to resign and return to 'secular' employment, as less compromising to his religious profession than a sphere in which he had overwhelming temptations to find sexual pleasure in the infliction of corporal punishment on the pupils of his school. Likewise, the masochistic pervert can enjoy sexual excitement by methods of self-flagellation, and yet in all other respects be a practising Christian disciple. Such facts only reinforce the plea we have been making throughout for co-operation between psychological medicine and religion.

One can readily appreciate, also, how easily marital problems may arise in circumstances in which either husband or wife is perverted in one of these ways. In such circumstances divorce, on grounds of cruelty or of 'incompatibility of temperament', may be the only alternative to life-long suffering for one or the other, if not for both. Such possibilities in regard to the nature of 'incompatibility' should be kept in mind as a point on which the minister should enquire when giving premarital instruction to an engaged couple. We can imagine the marriage of a sadistic husband being successful only if his wife is basically masochistic.

Exhibitionism and Curiosity

This is another contrasting pair of sexual abnormalities. The former is a tendency to 'show oneself off', and the latter to explore, if possible, the bodies of others, and be interested in the anatomical differences between the sexes. Curiosity, moreover, accounts for the somewhat embarrassing questions children ask regarding the origin of life, or where babies come from. These trends can persist also into adulthood in a sublimated form. Thus in a church which I have often attended, and in which I have sometimes preached, an 'usher' always made himself conspicuous by parading up and down the aisles, either to open or close windows, but he never did so until the congregation had assembled, and the service had begun. He was always dressed meticulously, and in every respect resembled a typical exhibitionist. Indeed, the minister himself may indulge his exhibitionistic tendencies in unnecessary self-display in the pulpit. One cannot be too careful not to divert attention away from Christ to oneself. More of this is unconsciously done than we are aware of.

Exhibitionism is a serious matter when it becomes a definite form of sexual perversion. Nudist societies are composed of perverts of this type; and from time to time the minister will be interviewed by one who has got into trouble because of self-exposure in public places, or by troubled relatives on his behalf.

Curiosity, or 'observationism', as it is sometimes called, can also be a source of trouble as well as of morbid pleasure. Thus one person told me of an irresistible impulse he had during adolescence to 'peep' at members of the opposite sex as they dressed or undressed to bathe, and on other occasions as well. This was not ordinary curiosity; it was an obsession which he could not control. In early adolescence he often hid himself in a large press in the bathroom, through the keyhole of which he was able to 'peep' at the maid as she undressed to take her weekly bath.

As evidence of how strong obsessional morbid observationism may become I have in my possession a stack of letters written by observationists to girls who passed them on to me for comment. In many respects the sentiments expressed in these 'love-letters' reminded me of the sensuous language of the love poems in the Song of Songs; but they were accompanied by drawings and pictures of nude women which they had cut out of pornographic magazines. This type of literature, by the way,

K

is on the increase, and is one reason for the morbid interest in sexual matters, which, in one form or another, is characteristic of the age. There is urgent need that this whole subject be dealt with in a reasonable way by chaplains and teachers in schools in their attempt to carry through a programme of sex education; for, to a greater extent than is realized, pornographic magazines, and paperback books dealing more with sexual perversions than with the nature of sexuality proper, are being 'devoured' by senior pupils of both sexes.

Fetishism

This is an aberration in which sexual interest becomes attached exclusively to some non-sexual object, such as a pair of shoe heels, an old shawl, a silk handkerchief, or a piece of hair. It will be noticed how frequently a child who is passing through the weaning process attachs unusual value to some such object, and carries it around wherever she goes. Boys are similarly affected. It would be a mistake to insist that a child should stop this practice, for it meets some psychological need, and usually becomes outgrown anyhow if the person concerned is not compelled to give up its precious 'fetish'.

Psychiatrists explain that fetishism is a substitute source of comfort for the mother's breast; and it will be observed that nothing can become a suitable fetish which, in some respect, does not provide the same kind of comfort. In the words of Dr J. H. Hadfield: 'In all the cases of fetishism we have analysed the fetishistic object proved to be a breast-substitute; for the breast is the first love-object of the infant, even before the mother herself becomes so. This is obvious in the common fetishism for corsets which is a natural substitute; the fetishism for shoes is because of their duality, shape and the body-smell; for the hood of a perambulator because it is round and shiny; waterproof rubber coats are attractive, like shoes, because of the body-smell and shiny, smooth surface' (*Psychology and Mental Health*, p. 376).

This explanation of fetishism may appear far-fetched, but one person whom I interviewed years ago was found to be in considerable perplexity because, as he said, the only thing that ever stimulated him sexually was a pair of shoe heels on some-one who was walking in front of him along a street. It did not matter whether the person was a man or a woman. It was the heels themselves which aroused his interest.

Homosexuality

This, as the name indicates, is a strong sexual attraction to a person of the same sex. It is sometimes called 'inversion', and in women 'lesbianism'. Most homosexuals and lesbians suffer from a sense of inferiority and shame. This is due not only to the fact that they are different from others, but because some States regard any homosexual adventure as criminal conduct, punishable by imprisonment. This is no longer the case in Britain; nevertheless homosexual urges and behaviour will continue to be looked on with considerable abhorrence by those who are normally sexed. Some schoolboys have confessed to having had sexual experience with schoolgirls simply to prove to themselves that they are not homosexuals.

How is a pastor to deal with this type of problem when a church member makes 'confession' of some overt act of a homosexual kind?

He must not, of course, condone the act, especially if it has involved, as it often does, a minor. At the same time he must fulfil his pastoral responsibility by showing understanding in order that appropriate treatment may be provided.

Most likely the first question a homosexual will ask in an interview is whether there is any hope of a complete cure. No immediate reassuring answer can be given to this question; but the person's mind should forthwith be set at ease to some extent by telling him that this peculiarity is common, and that he must not condemn himself for it, or feel inferior, unless, of course, he has not been able to control it. The minister should now proceed to satisfy himself in regard to the origin of the urge. If it is traced back to his earliest years and he has never experienced normal sexual interest, then it is likely to be physiologically conditioned. A degree of femininity in his appearance and characteristics may confirm this estimate, it being understood that some homosexuals play the rôle of the female in a homosexual relationship. Having satisfied himself that the situation is one of inherent and ineradicable tendencies, then the spiritual adviser should address himself to the task of helping the person to accept himself, with this peculiarity, as fully as another person should be asked to accept normal sexuality in itself as an essential part of his personality. This self-acceptance will help to resolve conflicts and make possible self-control and sublimation.

One homosexual, who had been successfully controlling his emotions, explained how he had formed a friendship with an understanding young lady with whom he regularly went for walks and to entertainments. This, he said, provided him with a reasonable excuse for not going off with parties of his own sex where he would meet with overwhelming temptations. His friend knew that in the circumstances marriage would have been unwise; yet for his sake she was willing to maintain the friendship. This meant much to him; for one of the problems inverts have to face is that of sheer boredom and loneliness. This is why the homosexual may be observed wandering, apparently aimlessly, along a street. Actually he is on the lookout for some other homosexual with whom he can have an intimate talk and some companionship, though not necessarily for purposes of any morbid indulgence.

Homosexuality, however, may be conditioned psychologically rather than physiologically. When this is so, psychiatry can do much to cure it. Many, known to me, whose homosexual interest dated from 'affairs' with other boys in their schooldays, are now happily married, and declare that they have no interest of a homosexual kind. Sometimes, indeed, a person's heterosexual interest may be blocked and arrested by a fixation to their mother. This may be so strong as to prevent the formation of a normal friendship with a lady of marriageable age; and, of course, it puts marriage (which would unconsciously be felt to be an act of disloyalty to the mother) out of the question. This 'blocking' of normal sexual energy or 'libido', to use Freud's term, results either in a homosexual deviation or in the symptoms of one of the common neuroses. Some true homosexuals have attempted to cure themselves by the experience of marriage; but the experiment is usually found to be ill-advised, for it is difficult to see how the basic incompatibility which exists in such circumstances could be overcome.

Lesbianism is just as common as is homosexuality in men; and the impression one receives from interviews with those affected is that the emotional factor is even stronger in lesbians than in

homosexuals. Thus I recall the case of a girl who had become a
source of anxiety to her parents because of her extreme moodiness, solitariness, and a tendency to sit brooding all day beside
an upstairs window. She was receiving 'pills' from the doctor,
who apparently did not understand her problem. (It was in
the days when doctors received no adequate training in
psychiatry as a necessary medical qualification.) We found
that the girl was strongly lesbian and remained perched at the
window in hope of catching a glimpse of her companion,
without whose friendship, she said, she could not live. Love
letters passed between them each day.

Adolescents frequently experience 'crushes' not only on girl
friends, but also on much older women; but these feelings need
be no more than passing phases and are often due to a lack of
parental love.

One member of a most extraordinary lesbian pair, who was
greatly interested in theology and philosophy, often asked me
for an appointment, so as to discuss with her some perplexing
point in theology. Invariably, however, the conversation
turned, sooner or later, on her homosexual experiences and
interests. Thus on one occasion she told me of how she and
her partner had gone through a marriage ceremony, the ritual
of which was made up by themselves, and read at the 'service'
by another lesbian who had their confidence and understanding. After the ceremony had taken place, the happy couple
went off to the Continent on their 'honeymoon'. On the return
journey they decided to spend a few days in London. Here one
of them met an old friend and made an appointment to join
her later at tea, whereupon her companion became uncon-
trollably angry and threatened to fling herself under the wheels
of a passing bus.

We have said that homosexuals are often amongst the most
solitary individuals in a community. One reason for this is the
widespread prejudice and ignorance of society in regard to this
and other sexual abnormalities. Hence the importance of
public lectures, as well as personal counselling, dealing frankly
with such subjects, so that homosexuals and others whose sexual
life is abnormal may receive instruction regarding their
problems, and, even more especially, be helped to get rid of any
sense of shame they may have because they are different from

others in regard to sex life. If the deviations about which they worry are found to be the result of constitutional peculiarities, then they should be no more ashamed of these than they would be if they had been left-handed. No one is responsible for the basic elements in his temperament. These he has inherited.

To sublimate these tendencies—that is to turn them into healthy and fruitful service that can only benefit and never hurt anyone—should be the considered aim of every such sufferer. In this matter the counsellor should be able to give useful and sympathetic advice.

TEN

The New Morality

In recent years few subjects have given rise to more serious discussion in Church circles than what is called 'the new morality'. The term 'morality', of course, includes much more than sexual behaviour; but it is this aspect of the subject rather than any other, which has given rise to such widespread correspondence in the daily and religious press, as well as in radio and television broadcasts. It is also in this sense that 'the new morality' has been provoking such concern among ministers of religion and others who have to do with the education of the young. Psychiatrists, for example, join with Church leaders in the production of books on the subject, some of which expound and defend the newer attitudes, whilst others as strongly condemn them. With sometimes diametrically opposed points of view presented by both groups, many young people scarcely know where they stand. They desperately need clear guidance through a rational presentation of the case for Christian ethical standards. Ministers of religion, therefore, have a special responsibility to provide the enlightenment which is so greatly needed by present-day teenagers on this important subject.

Whilst 'the wind of change' in relation to sexual morality applies in particular to those outside the Church, yet it must not be assumed that church members are unaffected by it. In regard to the former, statistical surveys have been made in an attempt to assess the extent and complexity of the problem. The Kinsey Report describes conditions in the United States; and in many respects it is an alarming one. Michael Schofield's *The Sexual Behaviour of Young People* offers the results of a comparable survey in Britain. This book asserts that 11 per cent of sixteen-year-old boys and 30 per cent of eighteen-year-old girls are already 'experienced'. Reliable statistics, however, are difficult to obtain, even when these are most carefully gleaned. Furthermore, there is a tendency among certain types to exaggerate the gravity of this problem. Thus, for example, large numbers of church-going people, as well as those who are not connected with any church, are to some extent morbid in their attitude to sex. These will inevitably believe every unsupported rumour regarding the immoral practices of teenagers or others. In fact, such stories will provide for them one of their main sources of prurient pleasure. Hence their interest in spreading abroad these rumours, no matter how fantastic they may be. They will do so with evident delight, although they usually pose as people who are shocked to the depths of their being.

Non-church-going teenagers, however, are not totally depraved. Comparatively few of them carry 'the pill' in their school satchels—despite stories to the contrary. Furthermore, the majority of those usually classed as delinquents will respond to appeals and challenges for assistance to the needy in their community, such as the old, the destitute, and the handicapped; or for work on behalf of such charities as the 'Freedom From Hunger' organizations. Incidentally, this type of approach in order to enlist them for such services is much more likely to produce good results than any amount of 'Gospel' preaching.

Perhaps the most disquieting factor in regard to large numbers of teenagers who have drifted from the Church, or who were never church-attenders, is the absence of any sense of shame or guilt arising from gross sexual irregularities. Formerly, such conduct was *felt* to be wrong, and was followed by a sense of remorse and fear of public disfavour. Today the tendency seems to be to glory in it as a sign of maturity. Indeed, the defenders of the new morality frequently justify their conduct by arguing that no one can achieve complete maturity except through actual sex 'experience'.

We have said that young people who are closely connected with the Church, as well as those who have little use for organized religion, are influenced by the new morality. To be sure there is not the deliberate departure from traditional standards of morality by church-going teenagers that there seems to be amongst those outside the Church. In many quarters, however, the former have come to question the validity of conventional sexual morality as embodied in the precepts of religion, and supported by the Church. In particular, teenagers, whether church members or not, are no longer disposed to accept all that the Church teaches in regard to personal behaviour as once they did. They insist on maintaining some freedom regarding what they are to believe, and how they are to act. Any attempts at 'conditioning' are rejected and condemned.

This fear of 'indoctrination' is carried to great lengths by some parents who refuse to allow their children to attend Sunday school, or regular Church services. This is to make sure that what they finally believe and how they act will be determined not by early suggestion but by convictions freely established. It is questionable, however, whether the minds of young and old alike can be completely safeguarded against 'indoctrination'. How can this be, we may enquire, so long as we live in societies? For in these circumstances everyone becomes affected somehow by the particular culture that obtains in the society of which he is a member. Moreover, those who most strongly object to 'indoctrination' by the Church seem to have no objection to 'brain-washing' carried out by scientific humanists, agnostics, and atheists—all of whom seem to be at least as dogmatic as the most rigid of theologians. It has to be admitted, of course, that Christian education is often in the hands of incompetent teachers, and that these far too frequently concentrate on religious beliefs that are as crude as the Mormon teaching to the effect that God is a person who possesses 'body, blood, and flesh' like ourselves. Far too little attention is given by such teachers to the nature and importance for life of distinctive values as enshrined in the teaching of Jesus.

Perhaps no statement expressing the impatience of some sections of youthful church members with conventional sex morality provoked more discussion than the book *Towards a Quaker View of Sex*. Although there are assertions in this document to which we would not readily subscribe, it should in fairness be stated that what these Quakers object to more than the 'old morality' is the methods by which the Church seeks to dragoon its young people into accepting every detail of traditional belief and moral practice, simply and solely on the authority of the Church. Thus the document states: 'We reject almost completely the traditional approach of the organized church to morality, with its supposition that it knows precisely what is right and wrong, and that this distinction can be made in terms of an external pattern of behaviour, and that the greatest good will come through universal adherence to the pattern.' Our answer to this assertion is that however sympathetic we may be towards the point of view here expressed, it must not be lost sight of that large numbers of young people are so constituted that they actually need rules of behaviour to be laid down for them in definite terms. These belong to the category of those to whom we have alluded in the section on obsessions. They are obsessional in temperament; which means that they are incapable of achieving any certainty in these matters, and are happiest when codes of conduct as well as specific beliefs are clearly laid down for them. Indeed, it is this psychological need, rather than real conviction, that has driven some, brought up in a liberal school, to embrace Roman Catholicism with all its dogmatism. For the remainder of this chapter we shall call the attention of ministers to the importance of discussing the difficult subject of sex morality in the context of certain fundamental principles. Five of these seem to be particularly relevant, and if thought out in group discussion, or indeed in sermons, may lead to positive results.

(a) People should be left in no doubt regarding the *naturalness* and *sacredness* of the sexual impulses. Already this has received some attention in the section dealing with sexual perversions. It was there pointed out that many of these 'deviations' are due to the unwillingness or psychological inability of some to regard these impulses as an essential element in human nature. Thus to adopt a hostile attitude towards such cravings, or to equate them with guilt feelings, is to introduce unnecessary strain and conflict into one's life, and at the same time to inhibit the smooth development of the emotional life. Moreover, the growth of the spiritual life towards its goal in maturity becomes a psychological impossibility where misunderstanding in regard to the true nature of the sexual impulses exists either consciously or unconsciously. Indeed, as we have also briefly indicated when explaining the origin of sexual perversions, religious conversion so called may be little more than a psychological process through which sexual urges themselves are brought under repression as the chief cause of guilt. Thus the distinction between pseudo-conversion and a genuine Christian experience of conversion needs to be kept in mind constantly by the minister in his pastoral relationship with people in spiritual trouble. For it ought to be obvious that no one can commit his total self to Christ whilst rejecting, as indecent, an important element in his God-given nature. Self-acceptance is a necessary condition of that surrender which is to result in personal integration and advance towards mature Christian selfhood, measured by nothing less than 'the full stature of Christ'.

It is difficult to understand why many Christians think of the sexual emotion as inherently wicked. Perhaps the explanation already given when discussing sexual perversions is here fundamental. Christian theology seems to have inherited something of the Gnostic heresy as to the essentially evil nature of matter, including the body and all bodily functions. Traces of this heresy are prominent in the Augustinian theological tradition, and, through it, in the promulgation of the wholly false idea that celibacy induces a higher form of saintliness than is possible in the marital relationship. It also explains, to some extent at least, certain extreme types of ascetic practices and other abnormalities of the religious life.

(b) Sexuality should be discussed in the *context of personal relationships*. This will serve to rule out the possibility of any purely selfish expression of the sex urge of the kind, for example, involved in prostitution, or in promiscuity. The former is degrading to both participants; and few, if any, would attempt to justify it. The latter may be based on a profession of love; but it is obviously the establishment of a merely temporary sex-relationship without either party assuming any responsibility for the ultimate wellbeing of the other. This practice, although not so degrading as prostitution, is, nevertheless, an expression of the same selfish attitude towards sex. It makes use of the bodies of others primarily for one's own satisfaction; and any such practice contradicts the Christian principle that we are always to regard the personalities of all others as ends in themselves, never merely as means. This applies to people of all races and every social status. It rules out as sinful, slavery, racial and religious discrimination, and even war, as well as sexual promiscuity. Let it not be forgotten that those who attempt to defend promiscuity may be responsible for setting the feet of others well on the road to prostitution, and therefore to moral and physical ruin.

Recognition of the inherent worth of every individual was a basic principle in the teaching of Jesus. Unless, therefore, we deliberately reject altogether, as mistaken or impracticable, the Christian standards of morality, we are committed to the principle of regarding the personalities of all others, as well as our own, as sacred, and therefore as ends in themselves and not as means to our own advantage or pleasure. It will be remembered in this connexion that Immanuel Kant included this same principle in his list of 'moral imperatives'. 'So act', he said, 'as to treat humanity, whether in thine own person or in that of another, in every case as an end withal, never as a means only.'

(c) The subject of sex, moreover, should be considered in the *context of marriage*. This means a definite commitment to the view that sexual indulgence outside the marriage relationship cannot be justified in any circumstance. The case in support of such a position, however, is no longer to be taken for granted. The present moral climate, indeed, does not make easy the acceptance of our traditional moral ideas, let alone our conventional sexual standards. They have to be examined and discussed with open-mindedness and candour. Otherwise we shall not only alienate still further those who are outside the Church, but increase the number of those within who, like the Quakers already referred to, will not tolerate anything that looks like an authoritarian laying down of the law.

So much is now being said on the other side through radio, television, and other mass media which is capturing the attention of young people, and is so much a subject of constant discussion among them, that ministers need to exhibit unusual patience, tact, and understanding, and a disposition to respect at least the views of those who are in the questioning mood. Nor should it be taken for granted that ultimately all will come right with our young people. Adolescents in particular are very sensitive to suggestion, and they tend to follow the leader or dominant person in their circle. It should also be understood that no group can hold together for any length of time without such a leader, and that what he stands for will seldom be called in question, as will most certainly the views of ministers, or others, who do not belong to the particular 'herd'.

The most widely-discussed aspect of 'permissive morality' is that concerning the rights and the wrongs of premarital physical sex intimacies. The arguments used in favour of this are not always easy to meet. The following is a short summary of those most commonly produced by teenagers: Young people of today are more mature than those of similar age a couple of generations ago, and are, therefore, ready for marriage at an earlier age. A strong point is also made to the effect that those who feel it harmless to indulge in premarital sex experience are deeply in love with each other and that they intend to marry in due course. The marriage, however, must be delayed for economic reasons; and the plea advanced is that the strain thus placed on the emotional and nervous life of those concerned is injurious to their health. Furthermore, it is asked, why should a ceremony which occupies only a few minutes make all that difference? Why, in other words, should sexual experience after a short marriage service be regarded as right, but be so heinously wrong if it takes place a few hours prior to this event? Moreover, to insist on strict adherence to the traditional teaching of the Church on this matter carries the implication that chastity is more important than love.

Perhaps, however, the most plausible of all arguments used in defence of the practice we are considering is the importance of making sure that those who intend to marry are sexually compatible. Many, it is pointed out, have discovered after marriage that they are sexually unsuited to each other; and when this happens the result is disastrous to both, so far as their happiness is concerned. The only way by which such a calamity can be avoided, it is alleged, is to indulge in sexual intercourse prior to marriage.

Before attempting to meet specifically the foregoing arguments, the minister might very well raise the whole matter of the specious subtlety of rationalization, and of the danger of being influenced by unconcious, or mixed, motives. Thus one's interpretation of the values of right and wrong may very well be affected by selfish factors which are unrealized because they lie beneath the conscious levels of the mind. It should be understood, for example, that the 'new morality' may be quite unintentionally self-centred—the individual often deciding for himself what is right, without due regard to the real welfare of his friend, who may be cajoled into acquiescing in the other's point of view, or of 'going along with him'—to use the modern jargon.

Having regard to all such possibilities it may be beneficial to suggest the holding of a preliminary session at which the danger of confusing cogent reasoning with rationalizing may be discussed at length. This should be found useful as a preparation for further sessions on the particular arguments advanced. Indeed it may very well be that the preliminary session will have already so clarified some of the points raised that no further answer to these will be necessary. This will be all to the good, since it is better that young people should see for themselves any weaknesses in their arguments than that their invalidity should be pointed out to them in discussion.

The specific arguments which we have noted, as used by the defenders of the new morality, may at least be blunted by the following considerations on the other side: The argument that young people are more mature than those of their age in former generations is by no means generally accepted. It may be that they are more mature physically and in their knowledge of the facts of life; but is there any evidence that they are less selfish or more responsible than their predecessors of some generations back? And, of course, these, and other similar factors, are amongst the authentic signs of maturity. Already we have stated that sexual abstinence, according to medical opinion, does not injure one's health, especially if one's energies are finding an outlet in creative activities. Regarding the assertion that to forbid the physical expression of mutual love prior to marriage is to place a higher value on chastity than on love—a conclusion that would not be in accord with Christian teaching —the answer surely is that there are many other ways by which love is expressed besides sexual activity. Conceivably, one such way would be through the maintenance of chastity itself, until the marriage ceremony has taken place. Nor will such self-control prove intolerable to those who are in love with each other in the true sense, and have not been merely the subjects of romantic passion.

Perhaps the most convincing of all the considerations

advanced in favour of premarital sexual intimacies is that in this way alone can an effective safeguard be provided against the union of a pair who are sexually incompatible. Now this argument is not easy to answer; but the following points should go some distance in doing so. First, where such unsuitability actually exists, it should not be difficult to discover it during the normal processes of courtship. This is certainly true when one of the partners is a homosexual; and in no circumstances should a pair, incompatible in this respect, be advised to marry in the hope that afterwards sexual relationships would automatically become normal. But if the homosexual pattern is based on constitutional factors, there is no likelihood that this automatic adjustment will happen, and the minister, therefore, should urge those concerned, if they consult him, to take no such risk. Secondly, ministers are sometimes consulted by those who are in trouble because their marriage has never been consummated. What can possibly be the cause of such a problem? In our experience the factor which is most likely to be the explanation is that premarital intercourse, to which they may make confession, had repeatedly taken place, and this had formed a guilt and fear complex—although both will insist that they did not feel they were doing anything wrong. It is here that a process of rationalization can effectively convert a guilt factor into a neurotic symptom which may take the form of frigidity, or impotence, or a general sense of abhorrence on the part of either husband or wife to the sexual approach. Thirdly, the majority of those who admit participation in sexual intimacies before marriage will confess, if they are honest at all, that neither was able completely to give himself or herself in the sexual act to the other. Inhibitions have always to be reckoned with, although those concerned may succeed in persuading themselves otherwise. There is the fear, for example, of the act resulting in unintentional pregnancy, in spite of the use of contraceptives. Should this happen, what, it might be asked, is the effect likely to be on the child's attitude towards his parents, when he realizes that he has been an unwanted child? Participants in premarital sexual adventures should also consider whether, as a result, respect of each for the other may not be affected. Indeed, self-respect can also become undermined in this way. Either of these eventualities will most certainly contribute to unhappy married relationships. Furthermore, it should be asked whether even the wedding day and the honeymoon can really be the romantic occasions they should be, if marriage intimacies have been anticipated?

Finally, the question should be posed to those who argue in favour of sexual experimentation prior to marriage, whether they honestly believe that this will pay. Omitting any reference to Christian standards of morality, as well as Scripture quotations against such indulgence (which, incidentally, will not impress teenagers), they should be brought face to face with the lessons which *experience* teaches. It must clearly be kept in mind that young people, to a greater extent than is often realized, are influenced by the contention of scientific humanism that moral values are weakened and vitiated when founded on the precepts of religion and sustained by religious sanctions. We have, therefore, to take young people as we find them, and discuss this, and all other aspects of morality, from the position on which teenage groups stand when we meet them in encounter. Furthermore, we must listen to them rather than preach to them, or at them. Then in meeting their arguments we should repeatedly appeal to the lessons of *experience*. They are bound to listen to what *experience*, on *the whole*, and *in the long run*, has to say regarding the fulfilment of life.

(*d*) Sexuality should always be thought of, and discussed, in the *context of love*. Although we have already touched on this, it is important to emphasize it here, and to bring it to the notice of young people, many of whom have been accustomed to think of love only on a physical basis. In fact young people should be informed of the danger of what Freud called the 'divided libido'. This means that their love goes out to one person and their sexual urge towards another. Often the basis of this lies in the lingering impression that sex is an indecent element in human nature. This would explain the fact that love is often directed towards a person of refined personality who may be one's wife, whilst the sexual interest becomes centred on a person considered to be of inferior rank. Actually, integration of the sexual factor with the love sentiment should take place at the dawn of adolescence; but this does not always happen.

It is also important to make sure that young people should be clear in regard to the meaning of love. The difference between

it and other emotional states with which it is frequently confused should be discussed. For example, love is not to be
identified with romantic feeling, which is often based on physical
attraction. The romantic element is usually present in the
early stages of a love-relationship, especially when this arises
in adolescence. Then it can be so strong as almost to sweep a
pair off their feet. In these days, at any rate, young people 'in
love' seem to experience no inhibitions in regard to the expression of such feelings in crowded thoroughfares, oblivious
altogether of the fact that they are under public gaze. The fact
that these same young people do not appear nearly so amorous
in the years following their marriage shows that romantic
feeling, to which the Greeks gave the name *eros*, cannot last,
and must not, therefore, be confused with love. Nor must love
be mistaken for what the psychologists call 'transference'—an
emotional relationship which is liable to become overwhelming
when conditioned by a strong infantile fixation on a parent of
the opposite sex. This can be the explanation of marriages
between those who are quite unsuitable from the standpoint
of age, and which are seldom successful. The union that takes
place in such cicumstances may not be with a wife as such, but
with a mother-substitute, in which case disillusionment is
inevitable sooner or later. In fact no minister should marry a
pair who are seriously incompatible so far as age is concerned
without thoroughly investigating the motives involved.

Love, moreover, can be confused with 'possessiveness'. This
latter has all the appearance of real love, the husband and wife
being almost inseparable. Usually, however, there is a history
of conflict and quarrelling behind this semblance of an
abnormal love-relationship, the possessive individual being
unwilling to allow his or her partner to maintain any independence or form any close friendships with members of the same
sex. Thus possessiveness is of the essence of selfishness, and is,
therefore, the opposite of real love, which is always concerned
with the welfare of the other person. The possessive person,
moreover, is always demanding attention and 'love' from his or
her partner. This, however, is a purely infantile attitude, since
love is something we give as well as receive.

True love, the love that lasts and that binds a pair together
'for better for worse', involves a total commitment of oneself

L

to another in mutual trust, and for the whole of life. It is obvious that such committal is possible only where those concerned recognize each other as worthy of such trust. This is why physical attraction alone can never be a sufficiently solid foundation for such commitment. An American student unburdened his mind to me on one occasion regarding the unhappy relationship that had developed between himself and his wife. I found that he had married her on the basis of her physical appeal alone; for she had been elected the 'Beauty Queen' of the State to which she belonged. This meant that she had many ardent suitors, each of whom was eager to marry her, without knowing anything regarding her temperament or character. Her husband discovered her utter selfishness after their marriage. Her demands he could not possibly satisfy; so they were on the point of seeking a divorce when our interview took place. Here we may recall the fact, already explained, that the paranoid personality is usually characterized by excessive jealousy and suspiciousness, that he can be strongly sexed and viciously cruel, and at the same time be psychologically incapable of experiencing, and therefore of manifesting, true love. But all these objectionable features of his personality he can succeed in concealing from his fiancée and her family, who will have no doubt that the man will make an ideal husband and father. Not until after marriage, and probably during the honeymoon period, will the person's real temperament become manifest, to the utter dismay and bewilderment of the bride. And let it be appreciated fully that there is less likelihood that marriage will cure the paranoid personality than that it will render a homosexual individual normal.

If a person is truly paranoid, deterioration, rather than any improvement in his reactions, is likely to take place. The leopard does not change his spots; neither does the paranoic his symptoms.

All this has to do with the importance of character as a factor in making happy marriage relationships possible. For, as we have intimated, there can be no full commitment of each to the other in which true love finds expression, unless each is sure that the other is trustworthy; and it takes time to make sure of this. Beauty Queens may not be very stable personalities; paranoid individuals are never sufficiently integrated to be ideal life-partners for anyone.

(*e*) Sexuality should be considered and discussed within the *context of home and family life*. In one's thinking it should never be divorced from the procreation of children and the establishment of healthy home life. Thus love should be child-centred rather than sex-centred. Otherwise the danger of mutual selfishness developing within marriage becomes a serious possibility—an eventuality which could be prevented by the adoption of one or more children. Moreover, whilst one can understand why procreation is delayed by those whose economic resources are limited, this, if unduly prolonged, may have serious consequences on the mutual relationships of husband and wife. It means that the sex act can never be carried out with perfect spontaneity. This, if prolonged, may result in frustration, and in the end produce some of the characteristic symptoms of hysteria. On the other hand the advent of a child will enable the parents to give expression to their paternal and maternal emotions, and introduce into their home life interest and purpose otherwise impossible. It should be understood, of course, that procreation is not the sole legitimate justification for sexual indulgence within marriage. The sexual act itself can have the effect of drawing husband and wife closer to each other, and of deepening and enriching their mutual love.

To bring children into the world, however, is a heavy responsibility, since, unless cared for, surrounded with an atmosphere free from strain, and carefully nurtured, children may easily bring to the parents anxiety and shame rather than joy and pride. For this reason no greater service can be rendered by the pastor than to establish, as a regular part of his weekly church programme of activities, young parents' fellowships, and to make sure that the instruction given to them on the rearing of children, and the advice offered in answer to the questions of parents, are provided by experts in child psychology. The minister himself, of course, will give much-needed guidance out of his knowledge of child psychology as well as from his own experience. But the additional help of the expert should also be sought occasionally. This is why we have included in this book a chapter on some fundamental principles to help parents to understand the factors which cause some of the common abnormalities that baffle them. For this reason also a chapter has been added on the Christian education of children, since it is here that we touch on the importance of prophylactics in family life. Some parents spend too much time in attempting to heal the symptoms of family illnesses, too little in the establishment of effective programmes aiming at the promotion of family health. The organization of parents' meetings is further desirable for the reason that so many parents are themselves scarcely out of their teens, and, whilst they may have attained a certain stage of physical and emotional maturity, they are often lacking in a sense of responsibility and parental knowledge. They need considerable enlightenment; but they also need to develop a sense of vocation as applied to home and family life, remembering that it is still true that these institutions are the foundations of stable society.

ELEVEN

The Normal and the Problem Child

Since ministers will frequently be called upon to give advice to parents who are concerned about the care and training of their children, an understanding of some of the main principles of child psychology must be a necessary part of ministerial equipment. In this chapter, therefore, we shall indicate some of the points that are stressed by child psychologists and psychiatrists regarding the psychological development of the normal child, and the main reasons for the failure of some children to attain normal maturation.

THE NORMAL CHILD

It is important for both ministers and parents to appreciate the different phases through which the normal child passes on his way to adulthood. These are roughly: (1) Years 1–2, during which the child is utterly helpless and dependent. Throughout this stage, more than any other, he must enjoy a sense of trust and security. No child who begins life in a home where there is tension and quarrelling can possibly mature normally. (2) The second phase includes the years 3–4. This has been called the period of aggression, for it is now that the child is becoming aware of his strength. He will rebel therefore against the demands of the parents. It cannot be too strongly stressed that this is a natural development and not a sign of abnormality, as some parents are inclined to suppose, especially if a child of this age raises his hand to his mother, as is often done. At this stage also the child who does not receive what he wants will fall into violent temper tantrums and make use of his tears to get his own way. Parents must be careful when children are passing through this stage not to lose their tempers—a difficult thing, particularly for a parent who herself may be a little hysterical and therefore emotionally immature. One of the main things to remember in this connexion is not to take too much notice of a child emotionally upset in this way. A little less concern and a determination to ignore the tantrum are wise precautions; for most children perpetuate this habit so as to gain the attention of the parent, as also to dominate other children in the home. (3) The age from 4–6 reveals less dependence on the mother, the father coming more fully into the picture. His presence seems to become more indispensable to the child—a fact which should help the father to be an example in all respects to his children. Failure on his part to be the ideal the child desires, and indeed believes him to be, prevents the awakening of trust which is an important factor in the development of a person's character. At this stage also the child shows interest in outsiders. He has his friends and playmates. These two factors—attachment to the father and to playmates of the same sex—are the natural homosexual phases through which emotional development passes, and to which reference has been made earlier. Interests also become multiple at this time. (4) The age 6–10 is best characterized as the 'conformity' stage. This is closely related to the stage immediately preceding; for the conformity has mainly to do with the child's relationships to other children. To their ways and desires he is likely to conform. (5) Between the ages 10–12 the child's world becomes shaken up. This is the transition stage in which one is being made over from childhood to adulthood. Already, in the section on schizophrenia, a brief account of adolescence was given in which the analogy of the Garden of Eden was used. Here, more than at any other period of the development of a youth, parents and ministers alike must be on their guard against mistakes. The phase of rebellion against authority (parental and ecclesiastical in particular), will increase, and religious doubts will arise. This is a time when parental displeasure and undue pressure must be avoided. Instead, understanding, patience, and *positive* guidance are called for. Let it be remembered that moodiness, restlessness, irritability, and the giving of 'back-talk' at this stage are all natural signs of development, and not of delinquency.

There are certain broad principles to be observed by parents in the effort to provide a suitable environment for their children. In the first place it should be remembered that love is needed throughout the entire period of maturation. The meaning of love in this connexion, however, has to be understood. It has been well defined as 'the active concern for the life and growth of that which we love' (*The Art of Loving*, p. 26). Another equally clear definition is, 'Love is feeling another person's needs to be as important as one's own.' The concern of parents to love like this will ensure that children will in turn find it easy to love others. Nothing can be conceived of as a more important preparation for marriage than the ability to respond to the love of another; and some are psychologically blocked from doing so. These are more sinned against than sinning.

Secondly, and following from the foregoing—the need to receive and give love—one should avoid the over-protection of children. This is how children are spoiled, and a spoilt child will have a difficult time at school, and indeed in life. This is due to the fact that he will always be demanding, and expecting people to treat him as an exceptional person. The twelve rules for spoiling a child, which were issued years ago by the Police Department in Houston, Texas, have been widely circulated. They are as follows:

(1) Begin at infancy to give the child everything he wants. In this way he will grow up to believe that the world owes him a living.

(2) When he picks up bad words laugh at him. This will will make him think he's cute.

(3) Never give him any spiritual training. Wait until he is 21 and then let him decide for himself.

(4) Avoid the use of the word 'wrong'. It may develop a guilt complex. This will condition him to believe later, when arrested for stealing a car, that society is against him and he is being persecuted.

(5) Pick up everything he leaves lying around, books, shoes, clothes. Do everything for him so that he will be experienced in throwing all responsibility on other people.

(6) Let him read any printed matter he can get his hands on. Be careful that the silverwear and drinking glasses are sterilized, but let his mind feed on garbage.

(7) Quarrel frequently in the presence of your children. In this way they will not be too shocked when the home is broken up later.

(8) Give a child all the spending money he wants. Never let him earn his own. Why should he have things as tough as you had them?

(9) Satisfy every craving for food, drink, and comfort. See that every sensual desire is gratified. Denial may lead to harmful frustration.

(10) Take his part against neighbours, teachers, policemen. They are all prejudiced against your child.

(11) When he gets into real trouble apologize for him yourself by saying 'I never could do anything with him.'

(12) Prepare for a life of grief. You will be likely to have it.

This could well be framed and set up in every home where there are young children. One of the main lessons which experience as well as psychology teaches in the development of children—especially on the emotional level—is that discipline must aim at the development of a positive ego-ideal or conscience, rather than a negative or morbid one. By negative and repressive attitudes one can be prevented from developing into a mature person, capable of thinking for oneself. This is to deny him real love.

In the moral training of children praise is as important as punishment, and indeed more so—praise, that is, when one behaves unselfishly and courageously. Corporal punishment should at all costs be avoided, since there is the danger in this way of awakening resentments which may permanently injure the personality. There are more effective ways of dealing with the faults of children than by corporal punishment. This is likely to be excessive when a parent has in his nature a strong element of either hysteria or sadism.

One way of correcting faults is to appreciate the power of 'empathy'. This is not the same as sympathy. Empathy means putting oneself in the position of another and trying to experience his feelings. It is a matter of the head as well as of the heart.

There is a story about a child called Dick who had a habit of paying no attention to what his parents said. They were particularly irritated by his determined and persistent refusal to come to his meals when called. One day his father offered to exchange places with him. He asked Dick to become 'Dad' and he (Dad) became 'Dick'. When it came to lunch time Dick (now playing the role of Dad) called his Dad (now representing Dick) to his meal. The latter paid no attention. The child called again and yet again but without response. Finally Dick got very angry with his Dad, but thereafter there always came a prompt reply from him when he was called to his lunch.

When a child gets into tantrums it is often a good plan to pretend that he is not the real child of the home, but a stranger. The parent may then start off looking for his real child and calling him by name. In a few moments the tears and tantrums end, and the child may be found slipping his hand into that of the parent and reassuring the parent that after all, he is his own child. The effect of such a method (which of course does not always work) will be to present to the child a positive ideal of what he is expected to be and how he is to behave.

PROBLEM CHILDREN

In considering this problem we are facing one of the greatest challenges that could possibly be experienced regarding the truth of the Christian belief in the existence and goodness of God. We have known some parents and young people to deny God's existence altogether, because one member of the home had been so seriously handicapped from birth that all possibility of normal development was ruled out from the beginning. There is another possibility in such circumstances. Instead of parents losing faith in God they may come to the conclusion that God is in this way punishing them for some sin committed by them—perhaps many years earlier. This is an impression which it is the first duty of the minister to correct. The question put to Christ on one occasion—'Master who did sin, this man or his parents, that he was born blind?'—reflects the same problem.

Problem children may be divided into three main categories —the physically handicapped, the mentally sub-normal, and the maladjusted. The physically handicapped include the blind, deaf, dumb, spastic, and deformed. These are all bound to suffer psychologically because they cannot take the place of a normal child in school life or in sport. They have to deny themselves so much that the average child enjoys that they need the utmost consideration from the community as well as from parents. The Church can and ought to make use of situations of this kind to help young people to cultivate the grace of sympathy and unselfish service. They should be taken to schools and institutions for the physically handicapped, so that as they witness the serious handicaps of other children they may develop a sense of appreciation of the gifts which they themselves enjoy.

More pathetic than the physically handicapped are those who are subnormal mentally. These cover a wide variety. There is the constitutionally ineducable child. This type has to be 'ascertained' as ineducable by the school medical services. In this regard great advances have been made in recent years through modern research both in psychiatry and pedagogic principles. Previously, a child ascertained to be incapable of profiting by any school programme was often committed for life to a mental institution. To do this on the basis of one series of tests, and only on one occasion, is no longer tolerated. In fact, many of those hitherto declared to be ineducable have been found to respond to some extent to new methods specially devised to help such children. The result is that it is now less certain than formerly that any children are completely incapable of making progress at all in mental development, and hope is being held out that further research into such problems will lead to still better results.

The mongol children are amongst those that differ most widely in both body and mind from normal children. On the physical side they are easily distinguishable. They all look alike in features, colour of the skin, and in body-build. They eyes protrude and the eyelids almost overlap. The tongue is large and tends to hang loosely from the mouth. In intelligence mongols are very limited. Formerly, they were ascertained as ineducable in an absoute sense; but in more recent years much has been done to draw out unsuspected latent powers and skills. Schools for children handicapped in this and other ways have been on the increase. Here, especially where a home atmosphere is provided for them, they make the maximum of progress. Parents often refuse to allow these children to leave their homes. They seem to love them all the more because of their inability to cope with life's demands; but in their child's own interest they should take advantage of the care and training now provided in every civilized country for children of this type.

One of the many signs of a more humane attitude to all handicapped children is the dropping of such derogatory names as idiocy, imbecility, mental defectives, and so on, in favour of one descriptive term such as 'a person suffering from arrested or incomplete development'.

In regard to the cause of such arrested or incomplete development there is, up to the present, little that can be said with certainty. Parents are likely to attribute the problem to some defect in themselves. They should at once be reassured regarding this. Here the minister can help them better than most others. Two or three children, for example, in every thousand born, are mongols, and this rate is fairly static, however conditions may vary. Thus it is that such children can be born to parents of any age. The most recent research into the cause of mongolity suggests that an extra chromosome exists in the mongol's body—a chromosome being a small particle in the nucleus of the cells that constitute living bodies. This means that a parent's worries or shock experience during pregnancy cannot be the cause (as is so often alleged) of this form of handicap.

Although a minister may be able to detect a serious handicap in the baby he is asked to baptize, it is not his place to inform the parents. At the same time his services will be very much needed when the parents first learn the actual facts. Many of these have described to us how shocked they were when the news was revealed to them by the nurse or doctor. Parents are the last to notice that their particular child has deviated seriously from normality, but they have to be informed; and then, in their depression and frustration, the minister's enlightened counselling will be of the utmost value. In the course of this he should refer to parents of other handicapped babies who were led, after a period of intense disappointment, to accept their child, not because his condition is the will of God, but as an opportunity for them to develop their own personalities in unselfish service. All ministers have known parents faced with this problem who, although formerly self-centred, have become amongst the most active social workers in the church, caring not only for their own child, but also for others

similarly affected. This is an illustration of how God can make
use of what appears to be a calamity so that parents thank him
for all that their child has done for them.

Another type of seriously handicapped child may be referred
to, and I can do nothing better than reproduce an account of
one of these as written by his mother. This is what she says:

This is the story of James and how his eighteen years of silent life
have brought an unbelievable richness to our lives, and gentleness
and thoughtfulness to his older brother. A much-desired second
son, his first seven months of healthy, happy infancy made our
family a joyful affair. An apparent simple cold, a soaring tem-
perature, convulsions increasing in intensity, and we had a baby
who no longer knew us or responded to sight or sound.

The inevitable round of specialists followed, but these agonizing
visits were sustained by a doctor friend who insisted we must seek
the truth and face it clear-eyed, but he himself was always in our
home as each hopeless visit ended.

Our greatest hurdle at this point was to accept that our child's
brain was grossly damaged, and this drew my husband and me
closely and strongly together as we told our friends clearly and
firmly what had happened.

Platitudinous optimism we discarded carefully, though it was
hard not to let ourselves believe it at times. Our friends accepted
the convulsing child, and seeing how we cared, came to care too
and admire the helpless beauty in the pram.

At the age of four years he began to recognize us, but could not
walk properly nor hear. At six years our constant doctor friend,
observing our elder son's anxieties, told us we must face the
decision to allow James to go to a residential school for handicapped children, or put an added stress on the life of the elder
asthmatic child. He also explained that a parting later in life
would be infinitely harder on James—increasingly aware and
dependent on us. This was the worst decision of all, but we let
James go after much prayer and soul-searching. Our prayers for
courage to face the world and home life again were answered
with such power that the wonder of this strength remains with us
still.

James today is without speech, epileptic, and with a most
limited understanding, but his beauty of face and body is matched
by the radiance of his smile and his embracing love for us and
those who care for him. Through him we have come to know
selfless noble Christian people whose lives are dedicated joyfully

to the care of handicapped children of all kinds. We have come to have as friends, not only other parents in similar circumstances, but people from all walks of life who, knowing James, have given so willingly of their talents to help build the home in which he and ninety other children live in an atmosphere of love, security, and Christian service.

MALADJUSTED CHILDREN

The maladjusted child constitutes a different problem from those we have been considering. For one thing, maladjusted children are often normal so far as their I.Q. is concerned. Some, however, are subnormal intellectually. They are often children who become delinquents and require 'special care' in an institution where they undergo discipline and appropriate training. They are frequently sent for such treatment under court order. That they are not merely of less than average intelligence, but have also suffered through parental neglect or mishandling, explains their anti-social behaviour. It is generally found that mental subnormality runs in families. An American book entitled *The Fruit of the Family Tree* contains impressive statistics in support of this. It raises the whole problem of heredity, and what modern eugenics has to say regarding this factor and its bearing on delinquency. Here, however, we are concerned more with those difficulties of behaviour, faults or character, and symptoms of emotional instability which are in the main the outcome of an unhealthy environment.

The over-anxious child, for example, is one who usually has had no adequate sense of security in infancy. Sometimes where the situation in his home has been particularly strained he may develop 'night terrors'. These are attacks of anxiety in which the child may appear to be assailed by some wild animal. He remains asleep throughout, however, and when the force of the attack subsides and he returns to a condition of calm, the memory of what had happened has completely disappeared. In such cases the home environment needs exploration, and if parents are not creating the proper atmosphere for their children it is the minister's place to help them to see the harm they are doing to their child. There is much truth in the statement 'There are no problem children; there are only problem parents.'

The adopted child is often maladjusted. This is usually due to the fact that he learns the truth regarding himself not from his foster-parents but from others, and not always in the most helpful way. An adopted child should be informed of the facts as soon as he is considered able to appreciate them. At the same time he should be told that he is loved at least as much as if he had been the real child of his parents. Happily in these days the regulations governing adoption are far more favourable to the welfare of the children of unmarried mothers than formerly, and there is, therefore, not the same danger that such children will feel unwanted by society as well as by those who have given birth to them. Here is yet another sphere in which the Church should concern itself, and not permit a stigma to rest on a child of unknown parentage, remembering that this is how delinquency is often caused.

It is extremely important that there should be no favouritism in family life. This is likely to happen especially when the parents are not themselves well-adjusted to each other. Then there is a danger of pairing off with some children and not with others. This is frequently the cause of that morbid brooding and withdrawal (autism) characteristic of some children. It is, at any rate, a factor to be considered when parents consult their minister in regard to a family problem of the type we are considering.

I shall finish this chapter by quoting from a letter about an adopted boy, written by his mother, who obviously had not the slightest understanding of the main problem in the boy's mind. Like so many others his difficulty lay in a disturbed emotional state. Here are the relevant excerpts:

John goes to school by bus and has recently become bus crazy. He has a season ticket and he believes this gives him the right to travel anywhere on the system. Quite often he is not home until 6.30, though released at 3.30. Once he did not come home until 9.30 after having spent the time joy-riding. His self-confidence is supreme. He is always calm and collected when he returns, and he never fails to return some time. About three weeks ago he was sleeping on a temporary couch as we had visitors. The first night, when my back was turned, he seized the opportunity to get up, dress himself and take the first bus into town, not returning until 10. The doctor thinks that if he had his tonsils removed it would take the restlessness out of him, and that he possibly would give up this habit. . . . It is, I think, a form of wander-lust. We are at our wit's end to know what to do. We fear that a time may come when John will go and will not return. The school authorities do not seem to understand him. Punishment by beating does no good. When threatened he promises to reform but he does not seem able to keep his promises. Those made at night are broken in the morning.

TWELVE

Christian Education

This subject is naturally suggested by the contents of the foregoing chapter. It raises the question as to what fundamental principles are to be observed in the promotion of Christian education amongst the children of church-going parents and others. That such teaching can affect the sentiments and characters of the rising generation there is no doubt. Here we have to remember that, compared with animals, which are generally creatures of physical and instinctive needs, the characters of human beings can be radically changed. This is because they are rational and have moral and spiritual potentialities. That is, they have been made in the image of God. One main purpose of *Christian* education ought to be the production, through such training, of distinctively Christian virtues and forms of behaviour. That efforts at organized Christian education in the day schools, and even in Sunday schools, has not had this result has been impressively brought home to all Christian educators in summer schools conferences, and in numerous books on the subject which have been multiplying in recent years. One book widely referred to in this connexion is Lord Acland's *We Teach Them Wrong*. This is a challenging book in which the author attacks Christian educators for concentrating so much on getting pupils to learn slabs of Scripture, instead of seeking to apply the main principles of Christian belief and ethics to their daily lives. This lesson has been reinforced by the fact that even though religious knowledge has been taught compulsorily in every school in Britain since 1944, yet the morals of the country have seriously deteriorated, and church-going has lamentably declined. In fact we hear much today of 'post-Christian Britain' as the true description of the actual situation and indeed some would assert that Britain is now an anti-Christian country.

In his treatise Lord Acland has not only criticized the failure of Christian educators to relate Christian teaching to life, but he has also much to say regarding the ineffective ways of presenting Christian truth, and the ambiguities and vagueness of much of the language commonly used. The listlessness of adolescents about which many teachers complain, and their expressions of doubt or even contempt for what is taught, only shows how honest many of these young people are as compared with those of the older generation, who still present Christian belief in crude forms and clumsy, meaningless language.

The outcome of all these strictures is that those responsible are concerned to introduce new methods of presenting the fundamentals of Christian knowledge, using and encouraging the 'discussion method' rather than the 'teaching method', for it has to be kept in mind that in order that such instruction may be effective the teacher needs to listen as well as to speak to his class. 'Honest to God' theology has brought into prominence the importance not only of being honest in the way we present Christian belief and standards of conduct to children, but also of avoiding the extreme anthropomorphism of the imagery we familiarly use in explaining what God is like, and how God acts. One would have thought, however, that no competent teacher has ever taken seriously the belief that God is a Figure located 'up there' or 'out there'. In the nature of the case, spatial metaphors cannot be wholly avoided in the presentation of Christian truth; but surely we did not need a Paul Tillich or even a famous prelate like Bishop Robinson to inform us that the finite cannot fully comprehend the Infinite. For, as a matter of fact, Christ Himself taught us to argue from the best we know in human experience to the nature of God as far beyond anything we can conceive. 'What man is there among you, who, if his son ask bread will give him a stone. . . . If ye then, being evil, know how to give good gifts unto your children, how much more shall your Heavenly Father. . . .'

Moreover, the restatement suggested by these 'modern' theologians is scarcely to be distinguished from the fundamental facts laid down by Christ in regard to the nature of God. That the underlying reality of the Universe is love, and that it is in the realm of personal loving relationships that we find confirmation of this basic Christian view of God, is the substance of our Lord's teaching.

In the interests of truth, however, those of us who know the

M

facts must afirm that our modern 'agreed syllabuses' on Christian education, if properly understood and rightly used by teachers, are bound to make a difference to the effectiveness of the courses on this subject as taught in schools. These syllabuses usually begin, as they should, with the fact and teaching of the life of Christ. To this, then, are related the essential principles of Old and New Testament revelation. Moreover, the practical and up-to-date application to life of these principles has a vital place in all these new syllabuses; and well-devised introductory notes and hints make this quite clear. Yet, if Christian education is to have the desired effect there are some matters which need serious concern.

One of these is whether *denominational* teaching should have any place on the curricula of day schools. Is there not a tendency for insistence on this to vitiate the whole purpose of religious education as conceived by Lord Acland, and indeed by all progressive and deeply concerned Christian teachers? Surely the general effect of segregating children into special classes for catechetical instruction only perpetuates the impression that Christians are hopelessly divided amongst themselves. Moreover, the period allotted to this subject in the timetable is so limited that priorities should be considered. In this matter, who will dispute the fact that it is much more important to help mould Christian character than to build up and perpetuate denominational prejudices?

A second basic requirement is the importance of securing the full co-operation of the parents, the school, and the Church, in making the most of our opportunities to inculcate Christian ideals into children's minds. Christian education should be a combined operation.

Of the three influences, the home is by far the most potent. Therefore it should be brought home to Church members who are parents, how much harm they can do by criticism of churches, church members, and ministers, in the presence of their children of impressionable age. This should be pointed out to parents. In this same connexion we would underline a point made earlier, namely, that few activities or organizations in a church can do more good than young parents' societies, with talks and discussions on the psychological and spiritual training of the children. Where a family connected with a particular Church is exemplary, the parents, or at least one of them, should be asked to share their secrets in regard to attitudes and methods with the group as a whole. People who have children will listen to the child psychiatrist; but they will listen just as eagerly to a mother or father speaking from experience.

Enough has been said already regarding the work attempted in the interests of Christian education in day schools. It is necessary, however, to remind parents how important it is for them to collaborate with the teacher, not only in regard to this but also in respect of all matters that concern the real well-being of the pupils.

When we turn to the responsibility of the Church for the Christian education of its youth we touch on what is one of its most important functions—that of a teaching ministry. Whether, however, this function is always viewed in the larger context of home and school, is questionable. All three influences should be related as closely as possible. The minister's task is not to usurp the function of the ordinary teacher who is supposed to impart religious knowledge as he does other subjects, but to establish pastoral links with the school. Head-masters themselves have pointed out the importance of this in preserving the connexion between school and church. This is valuable simply because otherwise many children, especially in secondary schools, have no connexion with the Church, never attend Sunday school, and receive no Christian instruction in their homes.

With regard to the place of the Sunday school in Christian training, the effect of work done in this way largely depends on the extent to which Sunday school teachers are equipped for this task. Previously the qualifications of Sunday school teachers were lamentably poor. At present, one notices, however, a determined effort by Church leaders and Christian educators to correct the situation. For nothing could be more fatal to the cause of Christian education than that the points of view of the day-school teacher and those of the Sunday school teacher should seriously clash. This would only confuse the minds of the children.

Since Christian education is applicable to worship as well as to biblical and doctrinal instruction it is important that at the earliest possible age children should be brought to Church. Here, as example is more potent than precept, it is of vital importance that parents should not be content merely to encourage their children to attend services of worship regularly while they themselves occupy their time in the garden, or in excursions to the seaside. This absence of parents from church services, except perhaps on special occasions, suggests to the impressionable minds of the children that, after all, Christian worship is not of any great importance—even as a cultural exercise.

It needs to be made clear, moreover, that Christian education is of the greatest significance from the standpoint of worth-while evangelism. For there is the closest connexion between Christian education and the culture of the devotional life, as well as the production of Christian values. It is lack of this groundwork that is largely responsible for the disappointing results of evangelistic efforts when tested by their fruit in terms of Christian character and service.

There are, of course, those who emphasize that religion is too personal and subjective to be taught at all. Some, indeed, argue that even Sunday schools can do more harm than good, since they may create the impression that conversion does not matter, and that the important consideration is the attainment of Christian knowledge rather than commitment of one's life to Christ. This represents very superficial thinking, and has been condemned from time to time in books dealing with our subject. Thus as far back as 1927, when there appeared a striking resurgence of interest in Christian education, George W. Fiske, Professor of Religious Education in Oberlin School of Theology in the United States, wrote a book entitled *Purpose in Teaching Religion*. One chapter in this book was devoted to a discussion of the question 'Can Religion Be Taught?' He argued cogently that inasmuch as no one is born religious it seems perfectly plain that, in some sense, religion must be taught, that, in fact, Jesus was called 'Teacher' and that He could not have taught religion in its fundamental principles and in its applications, as He assuredly did, if it were not possible to do so. But it has to be recognized that there are more ways of teaching religion than one. Remembering that teaching is more than instruction, the effective Christian teachers will

follow Christ in the methods He used, for He taught by
example as well as by precept, and, of course, He taught with
profound conviction and not, as in the present situation, when
so many called to this task teach the religious syllabus, placed
in their hands, with a question mark regarding it all in their
minds.

But, of course, religion is more than a knowledge of the
historical facts on which religion is based, and it is also more
than the theological beliefs enshrined in religion—even when
these are taught with the warmth of personal experience and
conviction. Religion is, amongst other things, utter devotion
to the ideals for which Christ lived and died, and this means
the commitment of life to Him wholly, and for all time. But
how can this be done in and through the evangelism of the
Church unless the basic facts, and values of true religion have
been inculcated by convinced Christian teachers and appreciated by those whom they teach?

The teaching of religion is often compared to the teaching of
art. In a sense no one can teach art. No artist teacher can make
his pupil an artist, and similarly no teacher of religion can
make his pupil religious. Nevertheless, the artist can awaken
in his pupil the sense of beauty and provide him with the
technique of reproducing beauty. In the same way the teacher
of religion can, if the spirit of God is in his soul, teach the art
of Christian living. He can inspire his pupil with the love of
God, with justice, truth, and in some measure with the vision
of God. Though we cannot give our faith to our pupils, yet
our own faith—and they know whether it is genuine or
theoretical—can stimulate theirs. They must grow their own
faith through their own experience, but we can guide that
experience. We can teach them by projects to practice the
fine art of the Christ-life, and we can open for them avenues
of service in which they discover the joys of self-giving. Thus
religion is communicated through teaching; it is also con-
tagious and can be 'caught', and in the latter process—often
becoming a reality suddenly—nothing is more important than
the challenge of the Christ-life which is made, most forcibly,
through Christian example.

In his epoch-making book *Christian Nurture*, Horace Bushnell
posed the question: 'What is the true idea of Christian

Education?' And his answer was: 'That the child is to grow up a Christian, and never know himself as being otherwise.' This, in fact has been the case in large numbers of the greatest Christians amongst us, and it would be well if such a master-piece could be procured and made available for teachers of Christian education whether in day or Sunday schools.

Modern Christian education, if pursued according to the objectives set forth in most of the newer syllabuses, quite rightly stresses the fact that the cleavage that has so long obtained between the secular and the sacred must no longer be allowed to persist. It is seen that there is no validity in fitting secular and religious knowledge into two separate compartments of the mind with little relation between them. For education is not concerned with the mere teaching of specific subjects, secular or religious, but rather with the education of the personality of the child in all its manifold aspects. It also emphasizes the fact that the sphere in which one should exercise and apply his religion is not merely in the time of formal worship but in all life's activities whatever these may be. 'In whatever our eyes look upon, or our ears listen to, we have to do with God. In all the things that our hands handle we have to do with Him. In all our faculties of intellect, of will, of instinct, of conscience, of emotion, we are with and in God. It is as impossible, there-fore, to separate religious pedagogy and general pedagogy as it is to expel God from the world which continually flows from His creative hand.' (*The Religion of a Mature Mind*, p. 302.)

THIRTEEN

Ministering to the Aged, the Sick, and the Bereaved

In giving advice to his preachers in relation to their pastoral responsibilities, John Wesley's familiar words are worth recalling: 'Go,' he said, 'not to those who need you but to those who need you most.' Wesley, of course, had no intention of underestimating the importance of pastoral work amongst all sorts and conditions of people. His system of class-leaders, devised for the purpose of caring for his converts individually, bears witness to his concern for the spiritual oversight of every member in his Societies. At the same time Wesley realized that, as in all other areas of religious activity, there are also priorities in the field of pastoral work; and amongst those who in no circumstances should be neglected are the aged, the sick, and the bereaved.

THE AGED

Notable advances in medical science and in public health services, as well as a considerable raising of the standard of living, have appreciably increased the expectancy of life. It is now estimated that about twenty years have been added to the normal life-span. This, welcome as it is, has created many problems for the State, the medical profession and the Church. The problem, moreover, has become more complicated by the development in recent years of automation. This has led to compulsory retirement at sixty-five—long before the majority of people are physically unfit for work. This has made the added years of life, which in a real sense are a gift to mankind, empty, and without purpose. Some, of course, succeed in finding temporary light employment. For these, retirement may mean little more than a change of occupation, or a fresh beginning. But sooner or later these too will be forced to join the vast army of the elderly unemployed; and the extent to which these can be made happy in their years of retirement largely depends on whether they have been of the obsessional type whose interests have been completely focused on their work, and whose retirement, therefore, is likely to result in frustration, boredom and depression.

Apart from the special problems created by enforced premature retirement, many other considerations make the prospect of old age gloomy in the extreme. This stage of life, which in certain circumstances can be very bleak indeed, has power to cast its chilling effect far back into earlier years. At the conclusion of a lecture given in a United States university in which this subject received passing comment, a group of students gathered round to continue the discussion of this part of the lecture. I well recall with what intensity of emotion one student exclaimed, 'When I think of being old a creepy feeling runs up my spine.' Why such horror of getting old? Well, obviously, the physical helplessness of so many elderly people, and the mental deterioration of large numbers as well. Thus a variety of diseases which seldom affect the young or the middle-aged is liable to attack the aged, though young folk suffer from illnesses of a different kind. The young, however, have recuperative powers which the old lack. With the advance of years, special faculties suffer impairment. Hypertension becomes prevalent; and for these and other reasons insurance agents are slow to renew car insurances to those over seventy. Such restrictions add greatly to the frustrations and miseries of the aged. Memory also deteriorates; and there is a tendency to dwell wholly in the past and to idealize it. More recent experiences cannot be recalled whilst those of earlier years remain vividly in the memory. It is pitiable to listen to old people asking questions which they repeat a few minutes later, or reiterate the description of some situations. In many respects we become children again so far as helplessness is concerned. It is pathetic when those who have become obviously senile do not realize their condition. How changed, too, in appearance the old become compared with what they looked like in early life. One has only to compare a photograph of himself at fifteen with what he has become at sixty to suffer a considerable shock—especially if he has retained, as so many do, some of his early narcissism.

In his book, *The Circle of Life*, Kenneth Walker, eminent

surgeon and neurologist, wrote a passage which is worth quoting:

> A hundred different sayings remind us of life's brevity . . . beauty fades, strength departs, and with gathering speed old age approaches. We see it in the faces of our friends before we note it in our own; half of the world grows older, half younger whilst we remain the same. For a time we succeed in deceiving ourselves that we are younger than our years, but in the end we are forced to accept the evidence supplied to us by our mirrors, and by the candour of our friends. We also have graduated from youth, and are amongst the middle-aged. Most of us accept the discovery ungraciously, and with a sense of grievance. It is not so much that we protest against the fate that finally awaits us, as that we recoil from the deterioration of faculties which precedes it. If we were birds making a graceful swoop across a room, we would accept our sudden disappearance philosophically, but we are birds moulting feathers and staggering in our flight. It is the ignominious departure, the gracelessness of our exist, which disturbs us (p. 58).

Not everybody by any means fits into the gloomy picture which, according to certain writers, some old people present. Large numbers retain their youthful spirits to a great degree, also their physical health and mental powers. Nor do all elderly folk give up some form of useful work for the church and the community. Many, moreover, retain their interests and their friendships and even add to them. These are the type who have learned at an early stage of life to adjust themselves to the changes entailed by the passing years, and know how to accept the ups and down of life with resignation—sometimes even with a certain gaiety of spirit. Their Christian faith, as well as the habit of learning to accept the inevitable, has much to do with this.

Notwithstanding the fact, however, that many remain poised as they face old age with courage and resourcefulness, nevertheless it should be remembered that all need pastoral attention, and the majority special assistance, if their lot is to be as happy as it should be.

So far as their material needs and their physical health are concerned these are mainly the responsibility of the State and the medical profession. The former provides old-age and retirement pensions, and homes for those who are utterly dependent on charity. The chronically ill and the helpless are usually cared for in geriatric wards of hospitals where the attention of the medical and nursing staffs cannot be too warmly praised by the visiting minister.

The Church is responsible for the psychological and spiritual needs of the aged. Some denominations provide 'Eventide Homes' for those who relatives cannot manage to care for them in their own family circles. By furnishing their room with some of the contents of their former homes, and enabling them to mingle with others who have common interests and share the same religious outlook, the twilight years for large numbers are now peaceful and pleasant.

In the United States the Churches now combine to create villa centres where the aged live in close proximity to one another, and yet enjoy the independence of having their own homes, with many modern facilities. Each block of villas is provided by a particular denomination which takes a special interest in the spiritual and other needs of those who occupy them.

But the Church's responsibilities to the old should include much more than providing suitable homes for them. What they need even more than material aid is companionship and a sense of being wanted and loved. That relatives should see that such needs are met is important; but often these seem selfish and unconcerned about their aged kinsfolk; and whether or not this is so, it is the Church's privilege to minister to their needs, so that their isolationism and loneliness, their frustration and hopelessness may be alleviated.

There are, on the other hand, large numbers of old people still able to live in their own homes. The Church should organize appropriate committees, the membership of which should include some young people who would make themselves familiar with the conditions in which the aged live, whether in their own homes or in those provided by Church or State, and should become acquainted with their special needs. This ministry is one expression of the outreach of the Church in love to the community in the midst of which it stands. Outings in suitable weather should be organized for these, irrespective of the denomination to which they belong. Church members who have no way of getting to services of worship should be provided with means of transport. Social functions should be organized on Church premises, and recreational activities arranged where both men and women may discover an enriching fellowship.

In all this the minister must be ready to exercise leadership; and where there is such a vigorous social expression of the Gospel, the Church itself is sure to benefit in spiritual interest and vitality. The primary concern throughout, however, must be the caring of the old people or the 'senior citizens', as the Americans call them—for their own sakes.

THE SICK

In the earlier sections of this book considerable attention was devoted to the understanding and treatment of the major forms of non-organic illness; and only a passing reference was made to the Church's responsibility for the care of the physically ill, although pastoral work amongst the latter rightly absorbs much of the minister's time and attention. Here, therefore, we shall be concerned exclusively with somatic illness, and with the ways in which the minister can help in the recovery of those so afflicted.

Patients who manifest symptoms of organic illness which, in the opinion of the doctor, requires fuller investigation than he can give, are usually taken into hospital where testing can be thoroughly carried out, and treatment given. This procedure has many advantages. For one thing it allows the general practitioner more time to devote to his surgery duties and to patients who remain at home. It has also advantages from the patient's point of view—amongst them being the availability of the medical and nursing staff should any crisis arise that needs urgent attention. Thus both the family concerned and the patient himself should feel assured that every precaution is being taken until the crisis of illness has passed.

Ministers should fully appreciate their rôle in the sick-room, or hospital ward, compared with that of the doctor (although both are concerned with the health of the patient) and should recognize that they are co-operating towards that end. The doctor, however, concentrates on the organ or part of the body in which a disease is located; and only indirectly is he concerned with the *patient himself* as a person. The minister, on the other hand, is primarily interested in *the patient*, in his emotional reactions and his attitudes to his illness, and in any other factors that bear on his happiness and peace of mind. This is important; since, as indicated in the first chapter, health is a matter which involves the entire personality; and healing, therefore, applies not merely to an organ of the body but to the total self.

Because the minister thinks of the patient first of all as a person in need of understanding, empathy, hope, and faith so as to undergird his will to live, his rôle at the side of the doctor is by no means an unimportant one. In making contact, therefore, with a sick parishioner, the first duty of the minister is to encourage him to give full expression to any matters that are a source of worry to him. These may be related to urgent duties left undone; and such are most likely to affect those who adopt an obsessional attitude towards their work. They may have to do with family problems, or with grievances or resentments of long standing; or they may arise from uncertainty regarding the probable course of the illness, the difficulty of meeting expenses incurred, or the possibility of having to face the ordeal of an operation, and the hazards involved in this.

It is on such factors, and more especially the way in which the patient is reacting to them, that the minister should concentrate attention. He should engage in the fullest possible discussion with the patient and in a mutually appreciative fashion, thus helping to ease his mind of unnecessary tension. Sometimes mistakes are made unwittingly, even with good intentions, by ministers in their care of the sick. They should not, for example, try to bolster up the morale of the patient by references, or stories, relating to people who, in similar or even worse circumstances, displayed amazing courage—as, for example, in the case of Richard Dimbleby. Such courage is usually the outcome of a particularly balanced temperament, as well as of faith. Not all, however saintly, can achieve it; and a person's attempts to do so may result in devastating reactions of despair. The minister must understand his patient and be ready to accept him with his temperamental weaknesses as well as with his emotional needs.

A second mistake against which the pastor must be on his guard when visiting the sick is his use of religious clichés, or the repetition of texts of Scripture, or an appeal to the sufferer to 'cast his burden on the Lord', or to accept the will of God whatever this may involve. All this can take place in a few minutes at the bedside of a patient, and with little relevance to the person's immediate need; and it may leave him more empty and worried than ever. Let it be repeated that the care of the sick, especially the seriously ill, requires time, empathy, and a measure of psychological insight and understanding if it is to have a genuinely healing effect on the mind and spirit of the patient and of his relatives. Special pastoral problems arise in situations in which the illness is, in all probability, terminal. For example, there may be the concern of relatives that the patient should be informed of the seriousness of his illness. Should the minister, in such circumstances, take upon himself this responsibility, even when the family requests him to do so? Their purpose, of course, is to bring home to the patient the urgency of making a surrender of himself to Christ.

No minister should agree to accede to such a request without first having consulted the doctor concerned, and having received his permission. Doctors differ on the advisability of making any approach of this kind when the patient is *in extremis*. It may have the effect of seriously disturbing the person and possibly of precipitating the end. In any case it is usually unnecessary to acquaint the patient that the end is inevitable, and imminent. This he himself will most likely have concluded from his own symptoms as well as from the graver bearing of the relatives who visit him.

As for 'death-bed conversions', I question the genuineness of any profession of conversion based solely on fear. For me, at any rate, this impression has been often reinforced by the fact that when, as sometimes happens contrary to expectation, recovery takes place, then the so-called conversion was seen to have had no lasting effect. Pastoral evangelism amongst those who are seriously ill and not expected to recover should be no different from what it would be in more normal circumstances —essentially an appeal for commitment to Christ as a preparation for life rather than as an insurance policy against death and the hereafter. The minister's main objective as he stands by those who are dying must always be to convey to them a sense of the presence and love of God, and of the solace which this assurance gives. And this can usually be effected by deeds rather than by words. Not all ministers realize, for example, how much Gospel can be imparted to a patient through a sympathetic look and a hand-clasp which will convey empathy, tenderness, and the nearness of Christ to the sick, or how much healing can follow participation in Holy Communion—a means of grace which should frequently be observed at the bedside of all sick Church members who desire it, and not merely of those whose illness is believed to be terminal.

THE BEREAVED

Most ministers on entering a home of mourning find themselves at a loss to know what to say to the sorrow-stricken family. We have to speak so frequently in such situations that we easily fall into the habit of uttering words of comfort that may have little meaning for ourselves, or for them. To maintain over the years a genuine relationship of empathy with all sorts and conditions of people who are passing through deep waters of affliction is by no means easy, and can be achieved only by one who has managed to maintain sensitiveness to the needs of his people, especially those bereaved. We have used the term 'empathy' here, as before, since that word conveys something more than the more frequently used 'sympathy'. It means not merely a fellow-feeling, a purely emotional reaction to suffering, but also an identification of oneself with the person in distress, and an appreciation of all the changes which death brings about in a family bereft of a loved member. In certain circumstances, of course, death is a friend rather than a foe. It should be so regarded when the person taken is old and has left behind a commendable record of achievement. Most people do not wish to prolong lives that are a burden to themselves and to others. We have referred already to the aged who have become senile and of the pathos of their condition. Can we conceive what society would be like if death were not the universal fact that it is? It could only resemble one vast geriatric hospital, with people becoming progressively descrepit and senile, with little, if any, awareness even of their own existence. So all that a minister should do in offering condolence in a home where the deceased has fulfilled the full expectation of life and has served his generation faithfully, is to express appreciation of his influence and of his service to others.

More difficult will be any effective ministry where the deceased has been a cause of worry and shame to his relatives. In such circumstances the minister must at all costs maintain his integrity so far as any insincere allusions to the character of the one taken is concerned. He may, however, express sympathy with the bereaved, and use the occasion to elaborate a little on the lessons which life teaches us. Most ministers, however, will prefer in such circumstances to conduct a formal and brief service with no address at all. But what are we to do when we stand at the graveside and are expected to read the committal which assumes that the deceased is 'in the hands of God, and that no torment can touch him'? On one occasion when reading the burial service at the graveside of a man who was the father of several young children, but who had been a disgrace to them, and had brought on himself the disease from which he had died, I felt the words 'the Lord gave and the Lord hath taken away' would be out of place at that service, and I sought to bring home to his companions the degree to which they themselves had been responsible for the man's untimely death. I had reason afterwards to know that many of those concerned went home none too happy regarding the part they had played in hastening his decease, and the miseries which his family had passed through on his account. Some, indeed, stricken in conscience, found their way to me in contrition.

There is always tragedy where one who has as yet scarcely begun the pilgrimage of life is taken, or where one who seemed indispensable to the family and community is abruptly cut off by some accident. Here is an occasion for the expression of empathy into which the community will fully enter. Yet no one can say that such accidents bear any relation to the will of God; and no minister should give the impression in anything he may say by way of consolation that it does. It should be realized by the minister that families in bereavement always feel the loss of a loved one more keenly after the funeral service is over, when the visitation of friends falls away. It is much better, therefore, that he should return to the home of a stricken family several days after the funeral has taken place, than to go forthwith and then assume that further pastoral help is not needed. He should remember that quite frequently delayed reactions to the shock of the death of a loved one can develop, and become serious. These take a variety of forms well known to psychiatrists.

In my book *Disorders of the Emotional and Spiritual Life*, I called attention to the difference between grief and sorrow, the former being morbid sorrow. The following is a brief summary of the symptoms of grief:

(1) A conviction that the deceased is still alive. He will, therefore, be expected at meals as usual and his place will be reserved at the table. He may be thought of as away on a business errand but will return in the course of a week. Even slight hallucinations in which the loved one is in the room and is engaged in conversation with the bereaved may take place.

(2) The person may withdraw from social life and become hostile to former friends, even refusing to admit them to his home. He will also absent himself from church, although previously a regular and interested attender.

(3) Another type of reaction is the sudden development of unusual elation and over-activity, which, as we have seen earlier, we associate with manic-depressive psychosis. This, however, is not a true psychosis, but rather an expression of repressed grief. Ministers and neighbours who knew the bereaved in normal circumstances are often surprised at the apparent elation which he displays at the funeral of a very dear relative. This they may confuse with an expression of the man's robust Christian faith. They do not realize that it it is a distorted reaction to morbid sorrow, and are therefore surprised when at a later stage he relapses into a morose state and blames God for the affliction.

(4) Often, as a delayed reaction to grief, there emerges a distressing sense of guilt. This is expressed in self-accusations for wilful neglect of the deceased, or for harsh words used in times of irritation, for which now no amends can be made. Usually the kinds of neglect for which the bereaved blame themselves are grossly exaggerated in seriousness.

(5) Idealization of the deceased is frequent where relationships between husband and wife had been strained. Thus, a husband who had been callous towards his wife, may, after her

death, eulogize her good qualities beyond all recognition and even establish expensive memorials to her. He may also take to writing long letters in which his wife's character will be praised in the most glowing terms. These will be circulated amongst all her friends and acquaintances. A young minister who had never been on very friendly terms with his father insisted on delivering a fulsome address at the parent's funeral service, and on himself conducting the service throughout— a clear instance of a compensatory reaction. Another illustration of a similar type of reaction was that in which the father of a deceased son manifested his morbid sorrow by preoccupation with, and overvaluation of, objects which had belonged to his son. Thus he carefully guarded his son's suits of clothes, took them out on regular occasions, brushed them thoroughly, and then replaced them where they had always been kept. He also imitated many of his son's peculiar mannerisms. As we would expect, this father was afflicted with a guilt-complex owing to his ill-treatment of the boy in earlier years.

In addition to the guilt element as a cause of morbid sorrow, other factors have to be taken into account, as, for example, abnormal self-control, and even apparent indifference to the news of the loved one's death. This is most likely to ensue if the death was unexpected and had taken place in circumstances in which it was bound to have a traumatic effect. The apparent apathy, so far from representing the operation of an all-conquering faith, may be a symptom of repressed grief. The psychiatrist would explain how important it is for those so severely stricken to undergo an immediate catharsis through a period of intense weeping. There is healing value in this. Ministers, therefore, should assure patients convulsed in tears that there is nothing to be ashamed of in such a natural expression of their sorrow. Of course ministers ought to be able to sense when tears are a revelation of genuine distress and when they are merely theatrical.

A further helpful piece of advice which ministers should give to the grief-stricken relates to the importance of resuming their regular duties as quickly as possible. Failure to do so may result in self-involvement in one's miseries, and in the onset of a vareity of psychosomatic symptoms. Morbid sorrow can have the effect of rendering a person completely egocentric and entirely indifferent to the needs of others. This happened

N

in the case of one woman of affluent means who had suddenly lost her husband. She quickly manifested the withdrawal symptoms already referred to. After some talks I ventured to ask her to allow me to interview, each week, some troubled people in her home. She agreed. Later I requested her to offer tea to one who had come a considerable distance. In future all who came received the same hospitality. Then I further suggested how much good she could do by using her car occasionally to take a few of the most lonely members of the group for a drive. All this she undertook with increasing pleasure; and later on she was able, in company with other women, to carry out a programme of most valuable social activities which had the effect of restoring complete healthy-mindedness and introducing into her life a sense of purpose such as she had never previously experienced.

I have scarcely touched on the importance of a vital Christian faith as a means of preventing the development of such morbid reactions as we have here been concerned with. But even psychiatrists—especially those who have had a Christian background, or who have definite Christian convictions—recognize the importance of such a faith in the maintenance of emotional health, both in normal conditions and especially in a period of crisis. However, let no one be bewildered when a person of even saintly outlook temporarily succumbs to grief; for even the saints can be handicapped by a temperament which lacks poise, or by the presence of conflicts the nature of which they do not fully understand, and therefore have not been able to resolve. In such a situation the minister should not hesitate to advise relatives to seek psychiatric help, and to do so without delay. This, along with his own frequent visits and his acceptance of the person empathetically—along with his or her grief —will never fail to have a healing effect.

FOURTEEN

Confession, Penance, and Forgiveness

The value of confession as a means of relieving guilt has had widespread acknowledgement in penitential literature and also in pastoral psychology. Thus William James, writing on the subject in his *Varieties of Religious Experience*, says confession 'is part of the general system of purgation and cleansing which one feels oneself in need of, in order to be in right relations to one's deity. For him who confesses, shams are over and realities have begun; he has exteriorized his rottenness. If he has not actually got rid of it, he at least no longer smears it over with a hypo-critical show of virtue—he lives at least upon a basis of veracity. The complete decay of the practice of confession in Anglo-Saxon communities is a little hard to account for. Reformation action against popery is of course the historic explanation, for in popery confession went with penances and absolution, and other inadmissible practices. But on the side of the sinner himself it seems as if the need ought to have been too great to accept so summary a refusal of its satisfaction. One would think that in more men the shell of secrecy would have had to open, the pent-in abscess to burst and gain relief even though the ears that heard the confession were unworthy. The Catholic Church, for obvious utilitarian reasons, has substituted auri-cular confession to one priest for public confession. We English-speaking Protestants, in the general self-reliance and unsociability of our nature, seem to find it enough if we take God alone into our confidence' (p. 462).

Paul E. Johnson, a present-day American psychologist of recognized authority, gives expression to the same sentiments, as he also does to a further point made by Jung to the effect that the restraint of emotion is itself wrong. Thus he writes: 'Private self-restraint is as destructive as any secret, when we conceal something even from ourselves in deceptive ways that cover up and deny true feelings, whilst living a lie which separates us anxiously from others.' (*Pastoral Ministrations*, p. 83.)

It is of course our sense of self-respect which prevents that openness of mind and heart which is here advocated. Human nature being what it is, the gossiper revels in any scandalous rumours regarding others—including fellow church-members —and he takes a special delight in giving every story of the kind the widest possible publicity. But this few self-respecting individuals can tolerate. Hence their reluctance to 'come clean' in the presence of others regarding any matters which could conceivably be made to serve the morbid interests of scandalmongers. And, of course, we are familiar with the fact that any stories which reflect unfavourably on neighbours, or, for that matter, on fellow church-members lose nothing in their circulation from one person to another. Thus the saying 'open confession is good for the soul' can only be subscribed to with due qualifications.

We recall, in this connexion, the respects in which open confession advocated by the Oxford Group (as it was formerly called) often turned out to be devastating in its effects on those who, in the tense emotionalism of the moment, were induced to make them. On reflection in a 'cool hour' they found themselves overwhelmed with shame at what had happened.

The Methodist class-meeting also encouraged open confession amongst its members, and especially among young converts. Wesley had intended this institution to be an occasion not only for the sharing of experience but also for the imparting of instruction on Christian discipleship by the class-leader. Large numbers, however, preferred to 'give their testimonies' than to receive the instruction which they needed. Thus the class-meeting began to degenerate into an occasion for the repeated confession of sins to which the converts had been addicted prior to their conversion and this became more of an indulgence which they enjoyed than a means of grace. Many also made these stories as lurid as possible so as to satisfy the morbid interest of the group. Thus the more vile the besetting sins confessed the louder rang the alleluias of the group. On account of such abuses of an institution potentially beneficial, the class-meeting was finally replaced by healthier forms of fellowship which proved more conducive to the ends of spiritual maturity.

Likewise the history of public confessions in the Roman Catholic tradition has had a chequered career. At first, this was imposed on all penitents and was an extremely harsh form of discipline, but, as we shall see, confession in this form and for this purpose was at length abandoned and private confession took its place.

In regard to non-sacramental private confession, made either to one's minister or to a fellow church-member, this also presents its own special problems, one of the most common being that in which a person feels a compunction to acknowledge some act of disloyalty to a close relative—perhaps a husband or wife. What, it is asked by those who in such circumstances seek pastoral advice, is the reaction of the injured person likely to be? To this no simple answer is possible. All the circumstances have to be fully taken into account, together with the temperamental qualities of the relative concerned. We have known some confessions made in such circumstances, without the advice of one's spiritual advisor, to have had disastrous effects, whilst on other comparable situations the acknowledgement resulted in the establishment of much healthier and happier relationships between the two. One fact to be exploited by the spiritual director when faced with problems of this kind is that usually there are faults on both sides, and that in any case no one is entirely free from blame.

On balance, pastoral experience teaches the advisability of making confession of the wrong committed to the pastor alone, or to some other trustworthy person, for in fact the particular matter on a person's conscience may not be the source of his guilt at all. This may lie in the deeper levels of the mind. However, in the next chapter we shall be concerned with this and kindred problems. But of the releasing effects of confession as a means of assuaging a guilty conscience for sins knowingly committed there can be no doubt. In fact the minister himself may feel the need for such an unburdening of his mind to a fellow-minister. The 'pastor pastorum' ideal is a most important one in the brotherhood of the ministry.

Thus at a pastor's school in the United States at which part of a lecture was devoted to this subject, a minister afterwards sought an interview. This man confessed that his ministry had been a ghastly failure mainly as a result of his inability to maintain happy personal relationships with his officials or church members. He attributed his frustrations to a sin committed before his ordination, and to the fact that he had failed to heed the voice of his conscience which urged him to make confession, prior to ordination, to his bishop.

Having unburdened his soul fully and having experienced a prolonged abreaction he was helped to open his heart and receive the assurance of forgiveness—not only for the particular sin that had haunted him throughout the years, but also for the mistakes and failures which had spoiled his ministry. Then he made a strange request, namely, that I should re-ordain him. At this I demurred explaining again to him, what already he knew—the significance of ordination. He countered my objection by reminding me that ministers often go through the marriage ceremony with husbands and wives who had become reconciled after a period of estrangement, and all he needed, he said, was that I should, in like fashion, read again the order and form of service for ordination, and then lay my hands on his head in an act of re-dedication to the office and work of the ministry. This I consented to do. He then made a further request that I should accompany him for the service to his own church, which was a journey of forty miles away. This, he felt, would add greatly to the significance of the occasion for him. Actually, what he most desired was that his wife should join us in the service. So in his church, and in the presence of his wife, we went together through the solemn service. Thereafter, for many years we corresponded regularly. Seldom did he write without referring to the total transformation in which both his confession and the service afterwards had resulted, and also to the happiness and success which he was now experiencing in his work.

If for non-sacramental confession any biblical justification is necessary in addition to what experience teaches regarding its therapeutic and spiritual value then the well-known words in James 5[16] come to mind: 'Therefore confess your sins to one another, and pray for one another, and then you will be healed.'

PENANCE

Protestants, as William James reminded us, object to auricular confession on the ground that it is always associated with

penance and absolution. They would refuse to regard confession and penance as sacraments, acknowledging only two
sacraments as explicitly enjoined by Christ.

Penance has an interesting history in Catholic practice.
Some of the facts regarding it make painful, if also in some
respects interesting, reading. In pursuing the study of the
subject we commend J. T. McNeill's *Mediaeval Handbooks of
Penance*. From the records there presented, it is clear that at one
stage confession was not considered to be effective at all unless
made in public. It was thus, as already indicated, in itself a
form of discipline rather than a healing experience. Sometimes
the penitent was compelled to kneel in the presence of the congregation, the latter all standing. Thus attention was directed
to the sinner, who had also to wear sackcloth and apply ashes
to his face. This latter custom is still practised by Roman
Catholics, especially on Ash Wednesday. Frequently, disciplinary action for grave offences also took the form of temporary
or permanent excommunication. This continues to be practised in certain circumstances. Such extreme treatment of
transgressors, however, is not peculiar to Catholic forms of
discipline. Some evangelical sects of the ultra-narrow type
apply it to recalcitrant members.

Tertullian said that the chief aim of penance was to humiliate
the sinner. Hence the purpose not only of the wearing of sackcloth and the disfigurement of the face by smearing it with
ashes, but also the habit of fasting, and the uttering of groans
and outcries to God in a public assembly. Penitents were also
required to bow before presbyters and to kneel before those
'dear to God'.

A great advance was suggested by Origen in the matter of
discipline. He advocated consultation with 'a spiritual and
skilled physician' in the cure of souls. This sounds quite
modern; but Origen, as we know, though well abreast of his age
in this respect, was held under suspicion by the majority of
Church Fathers. Hence his suggestion was not adopted as a
substitute for the traditional methods of Church discipline.
However, the revolutionary idea advanced by him reflected some
misgiving among the Fathers in regard to traditional practices
of this nature. For one thing, in succeeding generations the
practice of making confession in secret gradually replaced

public confession, although acts of penance had still to be made overtly. Pope Leo the Great condemned public confession as likely to prevent people from coming forward to make confession at all. He was particularly concerned that 'scandalous sins' should not be confessed in public.

It was about this time also (the fifth century) that penance became a means whereby the grace of salvation was allegedly conveyed to a soul, and was therefore not merely a punishment for one's sins. From this, however, it was a simple step to the belief that priests had authority to forgive sins—to 'bind' and 'loose'. This placed unusual power in their hands, and it led to those abuses which with other causes resulted in the revolt known as the Reformation.

Penance remains as a condition of salvation amongst Roman Catholics down to the present, although in form and detail it has undergone changes. Fasting is still enjoined, but of a type that can scarcely be called fasting at all. For certainly modern 'fasting' is not the threat to the health of the aged, sick, and delicate that it was when a prolonged period of complete abstinence from food was prescribed as a form of penance. One can only pity those who are encouraged to suppose that their spiritual health requires excessive discipline that is often inappropriate to their condition. Thus any visitor to Rome may witness, as I myself did, an aged and delicate woman labouring slowly on hands and knees up the numerous steps of the Scala Sancta, kissing each step in the process.

In this matter of penance there exists a sharp contrast between Catholicism and Protestantism. The former stresses the importance of good works, along with faith, as a condition of salvation, whilst the latter emphasizes the principles, 'by faith alone', 'by grace alone'. Protestants, however, also attach great importance to good works, but always as the natural outworking of salvation, never as a condition of it. Roman Catholic theologians regard auricular confession, penance, and priestly absolution as the normal means of removing guilt (see for example, *The Priest and Mental Health*, O'Doherty and McGrath, p. 173).

Whilst Protestant theology of experience rejects penance as a required condition of salvation it underlines the importance of *repentance*, a term seldom mentioned in Roman Catholic theology, in spite of the fact that it is a basic New Testament term. Penance and penitence, or repentance, are by no means synonymous. The former, as we have indicated, is a form of discipline imposed by a priest, who adopts the attitude of judge in making the penitential acts proportionate to the gravity of the offence. Repentance is primarily a change of mental attitude, and it also designates a state of sorrow, or regretfulness. It is the result of serious self-examination, through which the awareness of sin and its acknowledgement in the spirit of contrition, takes place.

Repentance must not be confused with remorse. The latter, as W. B. Selbie reminded us, 'looks to the past with no feeling beyond one of vain regret, repentance looks to the future with hope', and St Thomas defines remorse as a 'false love unto oneself'. The attitude of Judas after the betrayal, and of Simon Peter after the threefold denial, represent the difference between remorse and repentance.

Another fact which is not always recognized is that genuine repentance is not only a condition of salvation but a continuing element in this experience. The modern religious Pharisee has no place for repentance in his religious profession and attitude. Hence he is also devoid of the grace of Christian humility.

It remains to say that there are certain types to whom penance and absolution must be utterly meaningless, for they do not experience any awareness of guilt. Our note on psychopathy, for example, makes this clear so far as psychopaths are concerned. These may be aware of the *fact* that they have committed an offence, but they are absolutely devoid of the *feeling* of guilt. Again, only to a very limited extent can certain types amongst the mentally ill benefit by these disciplines Nor, for that matter, can some in these categories experience penitence in any real sense. The pastor, in such circumstances, can only commit such to the love and mercy of God, and seek such help for them as psychiatry and general medicine can provide.

FORGIVENESS

In the foregoing pages it has been made clear that guilt is one of the most poignant elements in human experience, and that it is accountable for many and varied symptoms of neurotic illness. The psychiatrist can help a patient to see the connexion between his symptoms and the guilt complex to which these are related. He can bring the hidden guilt-producing facts to light so that the patient may appreciate how these are related to his illness. It is, however, the responsibility of the minister to help the patient (or the penitent whose guilt is rational and conscious) to experience the release which the Christian pastor knows is available in this and in no other way. In dealing with individuals who come to make confession, and are truly penitent, it is important that he should adopt an attitude of sympathetic understanding and not that of judge, and that he should accept the penitent completely *together with his sin*. If he adopts an attitude of aloofness and moral superiority then he fails to win the trust of the needy person. In giving absolution the priest is said to be God's representative, and absolution becomes valid whether or not the priest is himself known to be a morally imperfect individual. Such reasoning is difficult for Protestants to accept since it is assumed by them that their spiritual adviser must be a person of marked integrity. If he fails in this then his personal influence suffers, and his work as a healer of souls becomes ineffective.

It is necessary at this point to explain that other ways of attempting to solve one's sense of personal guilt, rather than through forgiveness, are attempted by an increasing number of those who, although they have been nurtured in the Christian way of life, repudiate its teaching in regard to the need of forgiveness. In doing so they make use of certain well-known psychological mechanisms as methods whereby the sense of guilt becomes blunted, or destroyed altogether. Indeed Christian people also, without realizing it, make use of these same psychological devices in an attempt to silence the voice of conscience. Four devices of the kind may here be mentioned and explained.

First, many, either consciously or unconsciously, attempt to destroy the super-ego which, as we have earlier seen, is the source of acute guilt.

There comes to my mind in this connexion the circumstances in which a lady carefully schooled in the Christian tradition, and actively engaged in church work during her teenage days, came under strong communistic influence during her university career. She was induced to abandon her Christian faith for Communism. This meant also embracing the communistic conception of morals which, she contended, was much more attractive and which—so far as she was concerned—had the effect of making her feel 'one hundred per cent emancipated.' Then one day, while in class, she was suddenly seized with what at first appeared to be an epileptic fit. Psychiatric treatment, however, revealed the fact that what appeared to be a typical epileptic fit was rather an hysterical attack. In the course of treatment she herself was able to connect her illness with her spiritual history and her conversion to Communism. She believed she had become 'emancipated', but the super-ego was still there to be reckoned with. We have earlier shown that it is not so easy as people imagine to get rid altogether of this punitive conscience. At any rate to attempt to do so as a substitute for forgiveness does not always work. It did not do so in the case just described.

Many make use of the *rationalizing mechanism* in an attempt to gain release from guilt feeling. This means that they endeavour to convince themselves that wrong is right and that, on the other hand, what in their heart of hearts they know to be right is in fact wrong.

The mechanism of *repression*, as a means of resolving guilt, is also now well known. Repression is an unconscious way of getting rid of unpleasant feelings and memories, in the sense that we are no longer aware of their existence. Thus the contents of our minds must include far more than we ourselves are aware of. We may, indeed, think of the unconscious as a sort of ante-room in which are stored those elements which would become offensive to our ethical sense if retained in consciousness. It should further be explained that no one can recall at will any impulses or memories that are repressed, although the dream life becomes a mirror through which these unconscious contents can be perceived and understood by the expert interpreter. One often wonders what the effect would be on the claimants to sinless perfection if they could be induced to submit to psychoanalytic treatment. The results could shock them and, perhaps, thereafter produce something of the grace of humility in their spirit and attitudes.

It has to be appreciated that guilt *feeling* can become

dissociated from the behaviour which originally produced it, so that whilst the guilt *fact* remains as a conscious memory the corresponding accusing feeling may cease to exist in awareness. This conceivably may make life tolerable, but then the guilt feeling, having now become a complex, is sure, sooner or later, to produce neurotic symptoms with disabling effects on the personality. Hence to repress guilt is not to have finished with it, and, therefore, this device for solving the guilt problem is no substitute for forgiveness.

Many use the mechanism of *projection*, as a method of resolving guilt feeling.

Already we have seen that hysterical patients place all responsibility for their disabilities on their environment; never will they admit themselves to be at fault in any way. But large numbers of so-called normal people, many of whom are active church workers, are also amongst the chronic fault-finders and carping critics of society. The fact is that such people are the subjects of guilt, frustration, and inferiority, and instead of acknowledging these and seeking help to deal with them in rational ways they project them on to others. To repeat the words of Dr J. H. Hadfield they 'personalize their unrecognized failings and they hate in others the faults to which they themselves are secretly addicted.' This process goes on in church life with disruptive effects, as every pastor knows from painful experience.

On enquiry it will be discovered that those who are archcritics usually profess not only conversion but, in many instances also, to have received 'the second blessing', but it cannot be overemphasized that such experiences are possible without knowing anything experientially regarding forgiveness. The test of a valid experience of forgiveness is whether the outcome can be seen in the fruit of love. Jesus said, when referring to the act of the woman who was a sinner in anointing his feet and wiping them with her hair: 'I tell you her great love proves that her many sins have been forgiven; where little has been forgiven little love is shown' (Luke 8⁴⁷).

ABSOLUTION

In the Catholic tradition, as already indicated, much is made of confession and penance as actual sacraments. Emphasis is also placed on absolution which is the sole prerogative of the priest. Churches in the Reformed tradition, on the other hand, go to the opposite extreme and discount the spiritual value of these rites altogether. These would admit only two sacraments —baptism and the Lord's Supper—as the only ones definitely enjoined by Christ Himself.

Protestants are particularly opposed to absolution, in the Catholic sense, as implying that it is the priest who takes it upon himself to forgive sins. Catholic theologians, of course, would repudiate this and would explain that the priest in absolution regards himself as God's representative. The fact is, they would add, that at the altar the priest becomes virtually non-existent and only God is really present. It is, therefore, God who speaks the word of absolution. In passing, one would like to know what are the implications of this view from the stand-point of the nature of God. In what sense is He located at the altar? Does He really take the place of the priest in any other sense than that in which He speaks through ministers, or indeed, as Evangelicals would contend, through godly laymen?

Not all who sincerely seek forgiveness can be quite sure that they have received it. Sometimes, we find, that this may be due to peoples' unconscious pride. Just as some are too self-respecting to accept charity, so they resist the acceptance of forgiveness as a gift and would much prefer to feel that in some sense they had earned or merited it. This is why the Catholic emphasis on the importance of good works as a condition of salvation makes an appeal to large numbers. An even greater hindrance to the knowledge of sins forgiven is the obsessional temperamental factor. As earlier explained, obsessionalists can be sure of nothing. They are victims of pathological doubt, and an element of this is very prevalent. It affects large numbers who are, quite properly, regarded as normal individuals. Now all such need some form of absolution so as to be sure that they are enjoying the favour of God. In what sense then can Protestant pastoral directors help such to this assurance? Catholics base assurance on the authoritative word of the priest, and thus the penitent is induced to accept his assurance. Thus is met the need of the obsessional individual with his problem of doubt. It is otherwise with the obsessional Protestant who depends so much on the 'inner voice', and on the 'witness of the Spirit who bears witness with our spirits that we are God's children'. John Wesley, we recall, has two sermons on this text and on it Methodists base their doctrine of assurance. Moreover, they rest themselves on the objective ground of God's love declared, and pledged, to penitents in the cross.

In some sense all Christians need absolution as the culminating act in religious services of confession and forgiveness. The majority find such in the general worship of the Church and especially in the Communion service, with its 'comfortable words' which, of course, are taken from the New Testament. Those with obsessional or other difficulties need, in addition, special pastoral direction, and then the assurance by the minister that they are the recipients of God's favour and forgiveness.

Finally, the pastor should make it plain to all who are sincere in their search for assurance that they will find in experience that no one who practises forgiveness in his relationships with others will have serious doubts in regard to his own forgiveness. 'For if you forgive others the wrongs they have done, your heavenly Father will also forgive you; but if you do not forgive others, then the wrongs you have done will not be forgiven by your Father' (Matthew 6[14-15]).

FIFTEEN

Pastoral Counselling

References hitherto made to this subject have occurred in the context of other topics, and have been of a general nature. It is necessary now to consider it in a more specific and sustained way, beginning with certain important assumptions.

The first of these is that no pastoral counselling is possible unless the person, having vainly attempted to solve the problem by himself, now acknowledges his need of expert help. A similar requirement, as has been already stated, is insisted on by Alcoholics Anonymous before undertaking the treatment, with their special techniques, of an alcoholic addict.

There are, of course, those who will seek an interview, not because they have any personal awareness of need, but simply to please members of their family who see the necessity to which sufferers themselves are oblivious.

Furthermore, it frequently happens that relatives succeed in persuading a counsellor, noted for his skill in this work, to visit their home, ostensibly on a friendly or social basis, but actually with the hope that by some magical method, he may gain the confidence and co-operation of the person concerned, and at least bring home to him some awareness of his real condition. Seldom, however, does this method succeed. On the contrary, it may complicate matters, especially if the person about whose condition there is concern is even slightly paranoid, or is the victim of a hysterical temperament. Such persons, as we have already explained, are of a suspicious nature; and the latter are adept in blaming others, whilst always evading personal responsibility for their misfortunes. Thus I recall having on one occasion made arrangements for a psychiatrist to visit (on the basis mentioned) the home of a paranoiac who had been threatening the life of his wife. The patient at once became suspicious, and throughout the visit he posed as the most genial and gentlemanly of husbands, thus making the psychiatrist's visit a sheer waste of time. On another occasion I was induced to spend a weekend in the home of an agitated obsessional patient—ostensibly as guest of the man's son, supposed to be a close college friend of mine. Being sufficiently astute to see through our plan, no sooner had I been introduced than he retired to his bedroom where he remained until I forced myself upon him amid many protests on his part. The atmosphere was one in which naturally very little could be expected from our conversation. However, I bluntly told him things he did not know regarding the nature of his illness. He had suspected cancer; so I relieved his mind by most dogmatically asserting that he had none of the symptoms of this disease, and that if he had he would not be so agitated and uncooperative as he was. He calmed down considerably, became interested, and asked for more information. Then he accompanied me to the dining room and sat with his family at a meal—a change of attitude which astounded his relatives. This kind of confrontation with an unwilling patient was, of course, risky, and is no model for any general procedure in attempts to help where patients are hostile to their doctor or minister. However, it may work in the case of certain types who, like this patient, have not completely lost insight. And one of the advantages which resulted from a first visit to this home was the greater understanding gained by the relatives in deciding future attitudes to, and treatment of, their patient.

The incident suggests the value of pastoral counselling not only for the sake of the patient, but also for that of the members of the family, who seldom understand the difference between the symptoms of a neurotic condition and those of a genuinely psychotic illness.

A second basic assumption on which counselling should proceed follows from the foregoing story. It is, as already stated so often, an imperative necessity that any minister who acts as counsellor should possess a thorough understanding of the differences between the symptoms of various types of neurotic and the mechanisms by which they are produced.

It is for this reason that we have given so much space to the descriptions of these manifestations of various morbid conditions. The minister's rôle, however, as we have so often stated, is not to attempt direct treatment of the patients; but, if he is to avoid giving advice which may do more harm than good, then the psychological equipment already outlined is a necessary qualification for his work as pastor. In this connexion every minister should be familiar with the basic needs of human nature and the extent to which the frustration of any of these affect his happiness, his relationships to other people, and, indeed, his nervous and spiritual health. Thus psychological knowledge is important, not merely because of the light it throws on the nature of specific symptoms and their origin, but also because it demands greater tact, patience, and understanding of the difficult people committed to our care.

During a visit to the United States I was asked to act as a member of a panel in a hospital where doctors and nurses had met to discuss nurse-patient relationships. These were not always by any means perfect. Many complaints were reaching the doctors in charge of wards regarding the lack of understanding and sympathy which some nurses display in handling certain types of patient, whilst in regard to others they undertake the most irksome duties in the spirit of a real vocation. The panel had before them, for example, the case of a nurse who was ideal in her work with all patients except very elderly women. We were informed that on the very day in which the panel session was being held complaints had reached the 'nurse professor' that this particular nurse had caused an elderly female patient, who had fractured a leg, to shriek with pain by the abrupt and clumsy way in which she turned her patient over in the bed. She exercised due care and gentleness in her treatment of all other types of patients, including elderly men, but seemed psychologically incapable of showing any consideration for the sufferings of elderly women. In the course of the interview it was discovered that she herself had been a victim of the cruelty of her own mother, who on several occasions succeeded, by subtly diabolical methods, in destroying the prospects of love and marriage held out to her daughter. She was thus a frustrated nurse and was making use of the mechanism of 'transference' as a means of releasing the repressed resentments she had against her own aged mother.

Thirdly, the pastoral counsellor should never lose sight of the fact that his main objective ought to be to bring the person concerned to a fuller stage of maturity than he has reached thus far. Ministers who are asked to deal with specific difficulties,

o

especially in regard to interpersonal relationships, should keep in mind the fact that to resolve a particular difficulty is not to heal the person; and that no alteration in circumstances is likely to result in future harmonious relations with others until the individual concerned gains insight into his own weaknesses and immaturities. And immaturity, alas, can be present amongst those who have a reputation for profound scholarship, and who have achieved a place of pre-eminence amongst their professional colleagues. On one occasion I attempted to help a disgruntled individual who had returned home from a position which he had held overseas. He had all manner of complaints to make regarding his colleagues, and at one point informed me that I could not possibly help him, because I was not familiar with the conditions in which he had to work. Knowing the man before he went abroad I could have predicted that, wherever he went, he would in a short time be at loggerheads with his colleagues. So I had to make it very plain that I was not interested in the conditions overseas of which he complained; but I was concerned rather for himself; and that what he most needed was light on the basic immaturity which was the cause of his irascibility, impetuosity, and utter lack of the co-operative spirit. Nowhere more than in helping to settle family disharmonies, does a minister need to keep in mind the fact that childishness on the part of either husband or wife will account for most of the trouble, rather than any particular incident.

CONFESSION AND COUNSELLING

Already the values and limitations of auricular confession have been discussed. It may help still further to bring these into relief if we distinguish between this spiritual exercise and pastoral counselling. Strictly speaking, as already stressed, the former is concerned with the easing of the burdens of guilt through confession, penance, and absolution. It is assumed that one who goes regularly to confession is a sinner in need of forgiveness; though, as is well known, many who go to confession may have no lively sense of guilt at all. The counsellee may also be worried regarding matters of conduct and feelings of guilt; but it should be realized that he does not merely stand, or kneel, before the father-confessor to acknowledge his sins and receive absolution. He may desire light on a variety of problems, some of which are personal, whilst others are matters of interpersonal relationships. He may have a perplexed and troubled mind, and may desire above all else, the presence of some person to whom he can unburden his heart. Moreover, a large proportion of those who will seek the counsellor's help will be subjects of neurotic symptoms, or be afflicted with *morbid* guilt rather than with guilty feelings which can be eased through confession. To attempt to deal with neurotic guilt by confession can, as already seen, only do harm; for it will drive the afflicted person in on himself more than ever. The business of the counsellor will be to help such troubled individuals to understand themselves, and in general to reach a fuller stage of maturity than what was evident before the interview took place.

DIRECTIVE AND NON-DIRECTIVE COUNSELLING

A distinction has been drawn between directive and non-directive counselling; though this terminology is not regarded by some as very appropriate. They would prefer some such expression as 'client-centred' counselling rather than non-directive counselling. However, the main point is that an important principle is involved whether or not the most apt terminology is used.

In directive counselling the pastor himself is much in evidence. When a needy person appears before him he feels it to be his business to ply him with questions; and he, far too quickly, begins to offer solutions to problems which he may not have completely understood. In non-directive, or client-centred, counselling it is the counsellee who is placed in the centre of the picture. He is the person who matters. His feelings, as well as the problems which bring him for help, must be appreciated. It is fatal to good counselling if the pastor-counsellor too prematurely offers solutions to problems before these are stated in detail. To do so will shake the confidence of the counsellee; and if, in addition, impatience, or lack of sympathy on the counsellor's part, is communicated to the counsellee, then the time spent together will most likely be fruitless. From this it will be gathered that the attitude of the counsellor should always be non-aggressive, and to a large extent passive. He will listen, exercise restraint so far as readiness to give advice is concerned, encourage the counsellee to add more and yet more detail to his story, and thus enable him to appreciate the problem more fully for himself. We have known perplexed people to gain the insight which they needed by self-revelation through the adoption of this method by the pastor. It is said that the Quaker silence is not only a condition of listening for a message from God, but also becomes a means of self-knowledge. Likewise, the strict psychoanalytic method in which the patient is placed on the analytic couch, and asked simply to recall as many significant or painful experiences as may throw light on his problem, is also one from which the pastor, in a person-to-person relationship with a parishioner, may learn much.

There is, however, a limit beyond which the listening or waiting attitude of the counsellor may produce embarrassment rather than assurance and help. Some patients who have been treated by strict Freudians tell me that at times no words are exchanged at all between the patient and the doctor. When the time allotted to the interview is over the doctor simply proceeds to make a further appointment. Though there may be 'method in his madness', yet the doctor himself is bound to realize that his patient will leave feeling frustrated rather than helped, and will not be easily induced to continue such treatment. Pastoral counselling must never go to such lengths. There must always be communication between counsellor and counsellee if the pastor is not to waste the time both of himself and his client. This means that neither the directive nor the non-directive method must be rigidly and exclusively adhered to. Rather a combination of the two appears to be at once both the least time-consuming and the most effective method to adopt.

Some problems which bring people to their minister for interviews may require immediate handling by the direct method. Premarital counselling, special difficulties of belief, and guidance in methods of dealing with members of various sects active in the community, for example, come within this category. Frequently, specific questions will be posed to the minister, arising from such circumstances. These are best answered by giving the precise information needed. On the other hand, there will often be complications in what appeared to be a simple and straightforward matter of faith, and such will require time and the application of the non-directive method of counselling.

Let us refer to two completely different problems presented by perplexed people, each of which required the use of both directive and non-directive counselling.

The first of these is contained in the following letter, written by one known to me as a typical scrupulant. Here are its contents: 'I sometimes wonder whether many Christians do not underrate the demands of God, whether we are not all called to more dedicated lives and to more self-sacrifice than is common (I am afraid I go in for very little). I expect to retire in five months' time, and I am now trying to plan a fairly full and active life, if I am spared. One of the things that I should like to do is to take a good holiday on the Continent. Now I sometimes feel that with so many people in real need of one kind or another, it would not be right to spend so much money in this way.

'On the other hand I am well aware that I am sometimes neurotic in my outlook. As against this, however, is the feeling that as a Christian I am pretty much of a "light-weight"; and that when it comes to the point I have never sacrificed much, if anything. I also wonder if God, indeed, is not asking me in my later years to take Christ's teaching at its face value. This is only one of a number of problems that arise from time to time. I have, I fear, at times an unbalanced attitude to religion and sometimes I find it difficult to pray.'

No one who has had experience of dealing with 'sick souls' will fail to appreciate that what this man chiefly needed was a thorough understanding of himself, so that he might be able to relate his problem to his obsessional tendencies. Otherwise, merely to guide him to a right decision in regard to this particular difficulty is only to ease his mind temporarily. Before long we may expect him back with some similar problem. A serious Christian principle, is, of course, involved in the particular quandary which he presented; but his main problem was that of an over-scrupulous conscience, and to this one had to direct attention, and in so doing use both methods of counselling.

The other person whose condition required considerable directive as well as some non-directive counselling was that of a man, sent by his minister, in a state of spiritual doubt and depression. This man had been regarded as a worthless alcoholic in his community. One night a religious tract was placed in his hand. This induced in him an intense sense of sin and spiritual concern based on the fear of Hell. Later on entering a mission hall where he had heard Gospel singing he experienced what was hailed as a 'sound conversion'. This gave him an immediate feeling of ecstasy, which, however, was short-lived. The depressive state that followed bordered on melancholia. He felt he was 'a lost soul' but could not explain why. As we talked I noticed that he had only three fingers on each hand. On my enquiring how this had happened he explained that he had been born like this and that there was only a corresponding number of toes on each foot. This led to an enquiry regarding ways in which such a handicap had affected his relationships to others. At this point I simply encouraged him to recall as many painful memories as possible relating to his disability. He was able to relive many of the experiences of shame he remembered when people stared curiously at his hands—experiences which caused him to withdraw more and more from society. We then concentrated on the relation of this to his alcoholic addiction. He soon came to see that what he had been seeking in his alcoholic fantasies was oblivion rather than any satisfaction from drink itself. Having become clearly aware of this, our next problem was to offer him a picture of God which was in complete contrast to the sadistic, threatening Being presented to him in the mission hall evangelism. Incidentally, this accounted for much of his hopelessness and morbidity. He was asked whether he could really trust and love an earthly father whom he dreaded. The implications of this for the kind of pseudo-conversion which he had experienced were taken to heart by him. There followed a brief explanation regarding the precise meaning and responsibilities of Christian discipleship. Little more in the nature of psychological or spiritual therapy was needed in order to help this man to achieve poise and to take his place in the fellowship and work of the church.

PERSONAL QUALITIES OF A COUNSELLOR

In discussions which take place on the subject of pastoral counselling one is frequently asked whether every minister has the gift of counselling. The answer seems to be that, as in the case of psychiatrists, some possess this gift to a greater extent than others; yet the gift is one which can be cultivated even by those who by temperament seem to be devoid of it. This adjustment, however, is not possible unless the minister takes his pastoral responsibilities seriously. Some ignore the pastoral concern altogether and spend their time in the discharge of executive duties. They refuse to pay pastoral calls and shrink from any involvement in people's personal problems. These have actually become mere executives rather than pastors, and as such not only are failing to exercise the vocation to which originally they committed themselves, but also miss much of the deeper satisfactions of the ministerial calling.

But what is the essential difference, from the standpoint of counselling, between the psychiatrist and the minister? It is this: the psychiatrist has, in the eyes of the counsellee, the standing of a doctor with expert qualifications, and his work is usually with patients who come to him with nervous or mental symptoms which he recognizes and treats. The minister, who also has, or ought to have, some training in psychiatry, has, with those interested in religion, an additional advantage—that of being the recognized representative of the Church, and, indeed, if he is in a real sense, 'a man for others' representative of Christ as well. This gives him, with certain types—especially Church members—an influence scarcely possible when the doctor-patient relationship is purely professional.

From this it follows that *integrity of character* and an emphatic attitude are of the greatest value in pastoral counselling. The importance of such qualifications becomes increasingly obvious to the pastor as more and more people in trouble seek his help. Typical of such interviews is the following. A lady in trouble asked for an interview. It was not the first of the kind that had taken place between us. So we were prepared to listen for a considerable period. She was encouraged to unburden her mind and so she began, 'You have inner resources, wisdom, and sympathy which I lack. I am, just now over-emotional, so that I cannot think clearly. I know I am unbalanced, and cannot decide what I should do.'

'Tell me all about it,' I said. So she referred to a pair of newcomers to the church who, she felt, were determined to belittle her and take over her functions. She spoke of them as crude and ignorant and instanced occasions when they took upon themselves duties which belonged exclusively to her as the responsible person in a particular department of church activity. She was filled with remorse that she had allowed these newcomers to 'ride rough-shod' over her and insult her as they did. The wound they had caused had been festering over weeks. Her sleep had become seriously disturbed and her 'brain' had 'become confused'. Intense hatred towards them had developed and she found it impossible to control this feeling. She had refused to speak to them as formerly, and had become quite 'rigid' in her attitude to them. All that she had so far received from those whom she had consulted was the advice simply to ignore them. This she said she could not do. The whole affair had become obsessional. 'It is never out of my mind. I have made myself and my home miserable as a result of this insult.'

Listening to her story with patience and empathy helped her to see the situation for herself in more balanced proportions. Then our conversation turned on the family and social background of the offending couple, stressing in particular the probability that their behaviour was compensatory for inferiority and frustrations, which we had reason to surmise were factors in their case. At any rate my counsellee came to see that the insult had not taken place of deliberate intent. This latter point was stressed and resulted in signs of better understanding and a change of attitude. Next she was asked to look at the matter more objectively and to regard the problem as one of interpersonal relationships on a broad basis. Suppose, I asked, that a different couple were involved in a similar situation how do you think, I asked, would you react? She now saw that she would have faced the particular issue at the time, and with courage. Instead she had begun to brood over it, to withdraw into herself and to nurse her grievance. Here I interjected the remark that God can take such incidents to teach us lessons which we could learn in no other way, and that perhaps she would in future know how to tackle any similar situation in a more rational and courageous way. She agreed.

But our counselling session was not over. Two lines of consideration remained. First, having known the counsellee, I asked her to explain why her reaction to the particular incident was characterized by such intensity of emotion and revulsion of feeling towards a pair who, after all, had been guilty only of an act of gross inconsiderateness, which, however, was admittedly unintentional. This led, of course, to an explanation of hysteria and the exaggerated reactions to which this gives rise. She then admitted that had she been quite normal nervously the incident would have appeared in a much less serious light. As she admitted herself: 'I suppose I would have given them a fool's pardon.'

The climax of our conversation was directed to some positive action on her part, and for her own sake as well as for that of her offenders. I suggested that to get rid of inner brooding and the nursing of her grievance which caused herself so much misery, she should invite those concerned to her home to talk over the particular church activity in which all were particularly interested, and to do so once a week until normal relationships had been re-established. Perhaps, I added, the incident may then be raised, in a cooler atmosphere, and talked over helpfully. This she agreed to do, and added, 'I shall speak to both of them on Sunday morning.'

Let us briefly touch on a few other important qualifications (in addition to patience, empathy, and psychological and spiritual insight) of good counselling.

One is that the pastor who is to take this work seriously should himself be free from complexes, frustrations, and obsessions. This is important, for many who undertake such work do so in part, and without knowing it, from a morbid motive. Young ministers might very well, as part of their training, be induced to undergo some psychoanalytic treatment with a view to gaining fuller insight into their own characters and personality trends than is otherwise possible. This, we know, is a requirement in some of the clinics where psychiatric training is being given.

In the next place, and to repeat what has already been

stated in the previous chapter, the counsellor must not adopt, in relation to a client, an authoritarian attitude. He must rather take his place beside the counsellee and learn to accept him fully with his grievances, as the confessor must accept the penitent *together with his sin.*

Furthermore, confidences reposed in the counsellor as well as in the confessor, must on no account be divulged. These are a sacred trust and to break a confidence may mean the virtual end of one's pastoral ministry, for few will open their minds to any minister whose integrity in this respect they doubt.

One further general qualification for successful pastoral counselling outweighs all others in importance: it is a deep and abiding conviction of the inherent value of every human soul, and its sacredness in the sight of God. How more forcibly can this be put than in a moving passage in the book written many years ago by Drs Worcester and McComb, to which reference was made in our opening chapter. This is the passage: 'One reward which has come to me has been a new knowledge of human nature, intimate access to the inner lives of innumerable men and women, which has given me a sense of the reality of the things of the spirit which no scepticism of man can shake. Another reward is a deeper understanding of the mind and life of Jesus, a sense of sympathy towards His mighty works and a faith in them which I could have gained in no other way.

'We clergymen perform the regular routine of our parochial duties, conducting services, devoting much of our time to work and engagements of doubtful value to any human being. We give ourselves with all the resources of our minds to the preparation of our sermons, and, looking back over a year's preaching, we seldom know whether anyone is better or happier for our words. But if, at the end of a year we can look back to a certain number of persons who have gained freedom and release from a sad and miserable existence as a result of our counsel and patient work, if we can recall drunkards whom we have reclaimed, unhappy and miserable homes which we have made happy, would-be suicides whom we have restrained from death, courage which we have imparted to despairing men and women and better courses in life which we have opened to them—such thoughts bring much consolation and give us a sense of the greatness of the ministry with its innumerable opportunities for service' (Introduction to *Body, Mind, and Spirit*).

A fitting conclusion to a book on pastoral practice!

Index